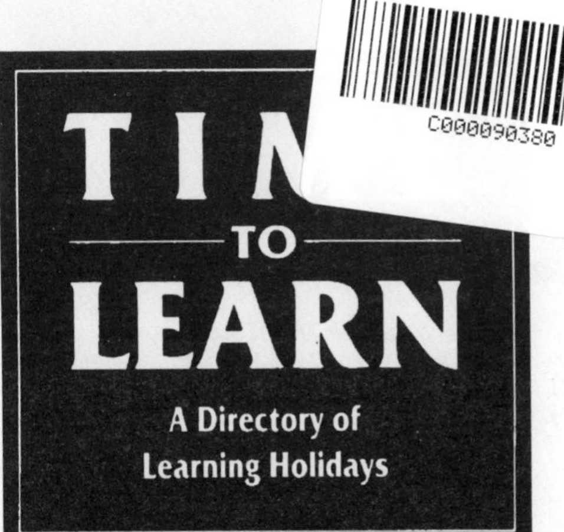
TIM
TO
LEARN
A Directory of
Learning Holidays

Published by the National Institute of Adult Continuing Education (England and Wales)
21 De Montfort Street
Leicester LE1 7GE
(Tel: 0116 255 1451)

British Library Cataloguing-in-Publication Data
A catalogue record for this book is available from the British Library
ISBN 1 86201 000 5
ISSN 0955-5374

Every effort has been made to ensure the accuracy of the contents of this publication. However, the information for this edition was collected during May 1996 and there may well be alterations to the dates, prices and locations of the learning holidays listed here. The organisers and NIACE expressly disclaim responsibility in law for negligence or any other cause of action whatsoever.

Text set in 8 on 9pt Univers by The Midlands Book Typesetting Company, Loughborough
Cover design by Richard Thumpston (Tel. 0116 270 5371)
Printed and bound in Great Britain by BPC Wheatons Ltd, Exeter
Distributed by Central Books Ltd, 99 Wallis Road, London E9 5LN

Contents

Published by the National Institute of Adult Continuing Education

How to choose your holiday using TIME TO LEARN

This edition covers from October 1996 to March 1997 inclusive.

Learning holidays at centres in Britain are listed in date order starting on page 11.

Study tours and learning holidays abroad are listed separately in date order starting on page 103.

If you have a special interest in mind

Each learning holiday is allocated a number. If you wish to look for a specific course (e.g. Découpage), look in the subject index starting on page 113 and it will give you a series of **course numbers** which you can then look up in the book.

What will it cost?

The fee quoted is only a guide to the price of tuition, accommodation and meals. You may find there are additional charges for such items as materials used, boat trips and entrance charges. An **AFD** in the fee column means **Ask For Details** and means that the organiser will supply you with details on request.

Conditions of booking

Always read these carefully before booking your learning holiday. Each centre has its own policy for **deposits, cancellations** and **refunds**. These are usually stated on the booking form.
It is advisable to arrange **insurance cover** against loss of fees due to cancellation.

Travel insurance is also required for study tours abroad and this is usually an additional charge. Please check that the policy provides adequate cover for all your needs.

For people with a physical disability

Some centres have access for wheelchairs, ground floor bedrooms or lifts. Centres offering such facilities are marked with the **wheelchair symbol** in the address list for organisers.

For people with a visual impairment

The **half-shaded eye symbol** is an indication of those centres who welcome people with a visual impairment to join their learning holidays.

For people with a hearing impairment

A few centres can accommodate people with a **hearing impairment.** The **ear symbol** appears against those organisers.

We advise you to discuss all your needs with the centres before booking.

A note from the publisher

NIACE makes every effort to compile the information in this directory accurately. We publish ***Time to Learn*** to promote the immense range and diversity of residential learning opportunities available in Britain and abroad.
However, NIACE is unable to investigate or accept any responsibility for the content, organisation or conduct of the learning holidays listed here.

Please direct all comments and enquiries to the appropriate centres. Names, addresses and telephone numbers of all the contributing organisers are listed on pages 6 - 9.

Use the **Learning Holiday Enquiry Coupons** on page 109 to make your enquiry.

Please remember to mention that you found the information in TIME TO LEARN

Learning Holiday Organisers

[wheelchair symbol] = Facilities for people with a physical disability
[eye symbol] = People with a visual impairment welcome
[ear symbol] = People with a hearing impairment welcome
ARCA = Member of the *Adult Residential Colleges Association*

Acorn Activities [wheelchair symbol]
PO Box 120
Hereford
HR4 8YB
Tel: 01432 830083
Fax: 01432 830110

Alston Hall Residential College [wheelchair symbol] [eye symbol]
Alston Lane
Longridge
Preston
Lancashire
PR3 3BP
Tel: 01772 784661
Fax: 01772 785835
ARCA

Ammerdown Centre [wheelchair symbol] [eye symbol]
Ammerdown
Radstock
Bath BA3 5SW
Tel: 01761 433709
Fax: 01761 433094

Andante Travels in Archaeology, Ancient History and Art
Grange Cottage
Winterbourne Dauntsey
Salisbury
SP4 6ER
Tel: 01980 610555
Fax: 01980 610002

Beaconhill [eye symbol]
East Kent Field Centre
Beaconhill Cottage
Great Mongeham
Deal, Kent
CT14 0HW
Tel/Fax: 01304 372809

Belstead House
Education and Conference Centre
Belstead
Ipswich
Suffolk
IP8 3NA
Tel: 01473 686321
Fax: 01473 686664
ARCA

Benslow Music Trust [wheelchair symbol]
Little Benslow Hills
Benslow Lane
Hitchin
Herts SG4 9RB
Tel: 01462 459446
Fax: 01462 440171
ARCA

Brasshouse Centre [eye symbol]
50 Sheepcote Street
Birmingham
B16 8AJ
Tel: 0121 643 0114
Fax: 0121 633 4782

Braziers Adult College [eye symbol]
Ipsden
Wallingford
Oxon
OX10 6AN
Tel: 01491 680221/680481
ARCA

British Institute of Florence
Palazzo Lanfredini
Lungarno Guicciardini 9
50125 Firenze
Italy
Tel: 00 39 55 284031
Fax: 00 39 55 289557

Burton Manor College 
Burton
South Wirral
Cheshire L64 5SJ
Tel: 0151 336 5172
Fax: 0151 336 6586
ARCA

Dartington Hall
Totnes
Devon
TQ9 6EL
Tel: 01803 866688
Fax: 01803 865551

Dillington House
Ilminster
Somerset TA19 9DT
Booking Secretary: Tel: 01460 55866
Tel: 01460 52427
Fax: 01460 52433
ARCA

The Earnley Concourse
Earnley
Chichester
Sussex
PO20 7JL
Tel: 01243 670392
Fax: 01243 670832
E-mail: earnley@interalpha.co.uk

Field Studies Council (FSC)
Head Office
Preston Montford
Shrewsbury
SY4 1HW
Tel: 01743 850674
Fax: 01743 850178

FSC Overseas
Montford Bridge
Shrewsbury
SY4 1HW
Tel: 01743 850164 and 850522 (24 hrs)
Fax: 01743 850599

Ford Castle
Ford
Berwick upon Tweed
Northumberland TD15 2PX
Tel: 01890 820257

The Gateway
Education and Arts Centre
Chester Street
Shrewsbury
SY1 1NB
Tel: 01743 355159/355137
Fax: 01743 358951

Hawkwood College
Stroud
Gloucestershire
GL6 7QW
Tel/Fax: 01453 759034
ARCA

Hawthorn Bridge
8 Pond Close
Harefield
Middlesex
UB9 6NG
Tel: 01895 824240

Higham Hall 
Bassenthwaite Lake
Cockermouth
Cumbria
CA13 9SH
Tel: 017687 76276
Fax: 017686 76013
Hearing loop available
ARCA

The Hill Residential College
Pen-y-Pound
Abergavenny
Gwent
NP7 7RP
Tel: 01873 855221
Fax: 01873 854817
ARCA

Hillcroft College
South Bank
Surbiton
Surrey KT6 6DF
Tel: 0181 399 2688

Horncastle College
Mareham Road
Horncastle
Lincs
LN9 6BW
Tel: 01507 522449
Fax: 01507 524382
ARCA

Knuston Hall Residential College
Irchester
Wellingborough
Northants
NN9 7EU
Tel: 01933 312104
Fax: 01933 57596
ARCA

Lancashire College
Southport Road
Chorley
Lancashire
PR7 1NB
Tel: 01257 276719
Fax: 01257 241370
ARCA

LSG Theme Holidays
201 Main Street
Thornton
Leicestershire
LE67 1AH
Tel/Fax: 01509 231713/239857
(24 hrs)

Maryland College
Woburn
Bedfordshire
MK17 9JD
Tel: 01525 292901
Fax: 01525 290058
ARCA

Meirionnydd Languages
Bodyfuddau
Trawsfynydd
Gwynedd LL41 4UW
Tel: 01766 540553

Missenden Abbey
Great Missenden
Buckinghamshire
HP16 0BD
Tel: 01494 890295/6
Fax: 01494 863697
ARCA

Oideas Gael
Gleann Cholm Cille
County Donegal
Southern Ireland
Tel: 00 353 73 30248
Email: oidsgael@iol.ie

The Old Rectory
Fittleworth
Pulborough
Sussex RH20 1HU
Tel/Fax: 01798 865306
ARCA

Pendrell Hall College of Residential Adult Education
Codsall Wood
Nr. Wolverhampton
WV8 1QP
Tel: 01902 434112
Fax: 01902 434117
ARCA

Pyke House
Upper Lake
Battle
East Sussex TN33 0AN
Tel: 01424 772495
Fax: 01424 775041
ARCA

Sing for Pleasure
25 Fryerning Lane
Ingatestone
Essex CM4 0DD
Tel/Fax: 01277 353691

Snowdonia National Park Study Centre
Plas Tan y Bwlch
Maentwrog
Blaenau Ffestiniog
Gwynedd LL41 3YU
Tel: 01766 590324/590334
Fax: 01766 590274
ARCA

Top Mark UK
12 Upton Gardens
Worthing
West Sussex BN13 1DA
Tel: 01903 526362

The University of Birmingham
School of Continuing Studies
Edgbaston
Birmingham
B15 2TT
Tel: 0121 414 5615/5605 (24 hours)
Fax: 0121 414 5619

University of Cambridge
Board of Continuing Education
Madingley Hall
Madingley
Cambridge CB3 8AQ
Tel: 01954 210636
Fax: 01954 210677

University of Manchester
Centre for the Development of
Continuing Education
Manchester
M13 9PL
Tel: 0161 275 3275
Fax: 0161 275 3300

University of Nottingham
Learn at Leisure
14 Shakespeare Street
Nottingham
NG1 4FQ
Tel: 0115 951 6526
Fax: 0115 947 2977

University of Oxford
Department for Continuing Education
1 Wellington Square
Oxford OX1 2JA
Tel: 01865 270360
Fax: 01865 270309

Urchfont Manor College
Urchfont
Devizes
Wiltshire
SN10 4RG
Tel: 01380 840495
Fax: 01380 840005
ARCA

Wansfell College
Theydon Bois
Epping
Essex
CM16 7LF
Tel: 01992 813027
Fax: 01992 814761
ARCA

Watercolour Weeks at Weobley
The Old Corner House
Weobley
Herefordshire HR4 8SA
Tel/Fax: 01544 318548
ARCA

Wedgwood Memorial College
Barlaston
Stoke on Trent
Staffs
ST12 9DG
Tel: 01782 372105
Fax: 01782 372393
ARCA

Wensum Lodge
King Street
Norwich
NR1 1QW
Tel: 01603 666021/2
Fax: 01603 765633
ARCA

West Dean College
West Dean
Chichester
West Sussex
PO18 0QZ
Tel: 01243 811301
Fax: 01243 811343
ARCA

Index to Advertisers

Winter Learning Holidays in Britain

■ ■ ■ ■

October 1996

□ □ □ □

1–3 October
1 Autumn flower arranging £76
Lancashire College, *Chorley*
ARCA

1–31 October
2 Basket making with cane £35*
3 Sugarcraft £35*
4 Eggcraft £35*
5 Flower arranging £35*
6 Bonsai £35*
7 Fabric sculpture £35*
8 Decorative interiors and paintwork £35*
9 Stencilling £35*
10 Needlecraft £35*
11 Strawcraft £35*
12 Machine knitting £35*
13 Patchwork and quilting £35*
14 Découpage – 3D £35*
15 Découpage – traditional £35*
16 Drawing, watercolours and oils £35*
17 Gardening skills £35*
18 Rush seating £35*
19 Cane seating £35*
20 Pottery – any Thursday £35*
21 Music – any instrument 2 hours £35*
22 Languages – one hour £15*
23 Birdwatching £40*
24 Furniture restoration – any 2 consecutive days £100
25 Woodwork – any 3 consecutive days £150
Acorn Activities, *Herefordshire, Shropshire and Wales*
****Per day. Bookings can be made for any number of days.***

3–6 October
26 Country walking with music £105
Beaconhill, *Deal, Kent*

3–6 October
27 Nettlecombe fungus foray £121
Field Studies Council at Nettlecombe Court, *Williton*

4–6 October
28 Industry archaeology and social history £175
Acorn Activities, *Herefordshire, Shropshire and Wales*

4–6 October
29 Bridge – the slam weekend £84
30 Therapeutic massage – women only £80
Alston Hall Residential College, *Preston*
ARCA

4–6 October
31 Gargoyles and misericords £95
32 Enjoying Jane Austen II £95
33 Calligraphy – a course in printmaking £95
Belstead House, *Ipswich*
ARCA

4–6 October
34 John Milsom choral weekend £110*
35 Elementary recorder ensemble £110*
Benslow Music Trust, *Hitchin*
ARCA
**Residential.*

4–6 October
36 Yoga and stress management £89
37 Dickens and 19th century England £89
Braziers, *Ipsden*
ARCA

4–6 October
38 Diploma in aromatherapy £AFD
39 Fit for life £95
Burton Manor College, *South Wirral*
ARCA

4–6 October
40 A weekend led by Jonathan Porritt £120*
41 German language and culture £115*
42 Heraldic illustration £120*
Dartington Hall, *Totnes, Devon*
**Residential.*

4–6 October
43 Quartet coaching £AFD
Dillington House, *Ilminster*
ARCA

4–6 October
44 Fungi £95
45 Wildlife garden design £95
46 Stone circles £95
Field Studies Council at Blencathra, *Keswick*

4–6 October
47 Calligraphy weekend £98
48 Wildlife through the microscope £98
49 Constable's painting and countryside £98
Field Studies Council at Flatford Mill, *Colchester*

4–6 October
50 Family wildlife weekend £260*
Field Studies Council at Juniper Hall, *Dorking*
**For 2 adults accompanied by 1 or 2 children.*

4–6 October
51 Fungi foray for beginners £90
52 Botanical illustration: autumn fruits and berries £90
Field Studies Council at Slapton Ley, *Kingsbridge*

4–6 October
53 Improve your duplicate bridge £135
Hawthorn Bridge, *Lyndhurst, Hants*

4–6 October
54 The Bach family £110
55 Memoir writing £110
Higham Hall, *Cockermouth*
ARCA

4–6 October
56 Intermediate Italian £84
57 Nature photography £84
The Hill Residential College, *Abergavenny*
ARCA

4–6 October
58 The Valley of the Kings £87
59 Pattern making techniques £87
60 The whiskies of Scotland £112
61 French conversation £87
Knuston Hall, *Irchester*
ARCA

4–6 October
62 Canvas work £86
Lancashire College, *Chorley*
ARCA

4–6 October
63 Quilt in a weekend – make a quillow £71–£99
64 20th century architecture – where now? £76–£105
Maryland College, *Woburn*
ARCA

4–6 October

65 Tchaikovsky: life and music £AFD
66 Autumn landscape painting £AFD
67 Machine embroidery £AFD
68 Alexander Technique £AFD
69 The Somme revisited £AFD
70 Visual arts – 1830–60 £AFD
71 Writing for the screen £AFD
72 French advanced £AFD
73 Water divining £AFD

Missenden Abbey, ***Great Missenden***
ARCA

4–6 October

74 The jazz phenomenon £AFD
75 Miniature painting £AFD
76 Chinese brush painting £AFD
77 Collage – Jacobean embroidery £AFD

The Old Rectory, ***Fittleworth***
ARCA

4–6 October

78 Cwrs Hanes Cymru (Welsh history) £68–£86
79 Gwneud Dillad/Sampleri Cymraeg £68–£86

Snowdonia National Park Centre, ***Maentwrog***
ARCA

4–6 October

80 Rocks, fossils and minerals £153

Univ Birmingham, ***Bromsgrove***

4–6 October

81 T S Elliot £AFD
82 Shakespeare: text to performance £AFD
83 Understanding community £AFD
84 Reading Latin £AFD

Univ Cambridge, ***Madingley Hall***

4–6 October

85 Castles in the landscape £60*

Univ Oxford, ***Oxford***
Tuition fee. Accommodation and meals available. — printed as: **Tuition fee. Accommodation and meals available.*

4–6 October

86 Stained glass workshop £AFD
87 Box framing £AFD
88 Travel writing £AFD

Urchfont Manor College, ***Devizes***
ARCA

4–6 October

89 3D cards and pictures £81
90 Advanced Spanish £82
91 The bloody games of ancient Rome £81
92 Photography: introduction to black and white printing £98

Wansfell College, ***Theydon Bois***
ARCA

4–6 October

93 Susie Cooper weekend £75

Wedgwood Memorial College, ***Barlaston***
ARCA

4–6 October

94 Solo singing workshop £184

Wensum Lodge, ***Norwich***
ARCA

4–6 October

95 Jewellery making in precious metals £AFD
96 Introduction to woodturning £AFD
97 Calligraphy for not-quite beginners £AFD
98 Watercolour for beginners £AFD
99 Basic blacksmithing £AFD
100 The Barbizon School – landscape painting in France 1820–1870 £AFD

West Dean College, ***Chichester***
ARCA

4–7 October

101 Calligraphy £142

Field Studies Council at Flatford Mill, ***Colchester***

4–7 October

102 Further techniques in miniature painting £AFD

West Dean College, ***Chichester***
ARCA

5–6 October
103 Decorative interiors and paintwork £70
104 Beadwork £70
105 Drawing for beginners £82
106 Pottery £70
Acorn Activities, *Herefordshire, Shropshire and Wales*

5–6 October
107 Batik – fabric decoration £21
108 Book conservation – cloth/leather book repair £30
The Gateway, *Shrewsbury*
Local accommodation is arranged separately on request.

5–7 October
109 Jane Austen and Bath £135
Univ Nottingham, *Bath*

6–11 October
110 Improve your watercolours £196
Field Studies Council at Flatford Mill, *Colchester*

6–11 October
111 Watercolour painting £AFD
Higham Hall, *Cockermouth*
ARCA

6–11 October
112 Repairing and refinishing antique furniture £AFD
113 Modelling, mouldmaking and casting for sculpture £AFD
114 Willow basketmaking, cane and rush seating £AFD
115 Autumn flower portraits in watercolour and gouache £AFD
West Dean College, *Chichester*
ARCA

6–12 October
116 Chairmaking – traditional Windsors, English and American ladderbacks £AFD
West Dean College, *Chichester*
ARCA

7–9 October
117 Bonnie Prince Charlie £81
Wansfell College, *Theydon Bois*
ARCA

7–11 October
118 Paint anything £AFD
119 October gardens £AFD
120 Cut and sew garment making £AFD
121 Ceramic restoration (stage one) £AFD
The Old Rectory, *Fittleworth*
ARCA

7–14 October
122 Geese, peat and malt whisky: autumn birdwatching on Islay £485
FSC Overseas, *Islay, Scotland*

10–13 October
123 Country village activities £105
Beaconhill, *Deal, Kent*

10–13 October
124 Out and about £125
Field Studies Council at Nettlecombe Court, *Williton*

10–13 October
125 Sign communication skills stage 1 module 1 £AFD
Lancashire College, *Chorley*
ARCA

10–14 October
126 Black and white photography £135
Field Studies Council at Dale Fort, *Haverfordwest*

11–12 October
127 George Orwell £110
128 Miniature painting £110
Higham Hall, *Cockermouth*
ARCA

11–13 October
129 Murder, mystery weekend £195
Acorn Activities, *Herefordshire, Shropshire and Wales*

11–13 October
130 Spinning £80
131 Painting on silk £80
Alston Hall Residential College, ***Preston***
ARCA

11–13 October
132 Elementary wind chamber music £110*
133 Musicosophia – the creative listener and the music of Anton Bruckner £110*
Benslow Music Trust, ***Hitchin***
ARCA
****Residential.***

11–13 October
134 Braziers/MENSA course: Nationalism and human nature £89
Braziers, ***Ipsden***
ARCA

11–13 October
135 Jewellery workshop £AFD
136 Colour slide printing £155
Burton Manor College, ***South Wirral***
ARCA

11–13 October
137 Autumn gardens £145*
138 Movement, massage and meditation £110*
Dartington Hall, ***Totnes, Devon***
****Residential.***

11–13 October
139 Autumn woodlands £95
Field Studies Council at Blencathra, ***Keswick***

11–13 October
140 Mosses £98
141 Life on the seashore £98
Field Studies Council at Flatford Mill, ***Colchester***

11–13 October
142 Photographing fungi £117*
143 Mosses and liverworts of the chalk and greensand £100
144 Mollusc course £96
Field Studies Council at Juniper Hall, ***Dorking***
****RPS members £97.***

11–13 October
145 Dowsing for beginners (British Society of Dowsers) £AFD
Hawkwood College, ***Stroud***
ARCA

11–13 October
146 Chinese brush painting £84
147 Grandma's grandma £84
148 Three choirs festival £84
The Hill Residential College, ***Abergavenny***
ARCA

11–13 October
149 Glasscraft £82
150 Bridge £82
Horncastle College, ***Horncastle***
ARCA

11–13 October
151 Computing with Windows £89
152 Learning German (a second stage) £87
153 The Civil War in the Midlands £87
154 Jane Austen £87
Knuston Hall, ***Irchester***
ARCA

11–13 October
155 Introduction to Russian poetry £55
Meirionnydd Languages, ***North Wales***

11–13 October
156 Tai Ji Quan £AFD
157 Chinese brush painting £AFD
158 Autumn painting workshop £AFD
159 Oil painting techniques for improvers £AFD
160 Your guide to tax under self-assessment £AFD
161 Two contemporary dramatists – Tom Stoppard and Alan Ayckbourn £AFD

Set in attractive grounds on the edge of a small market town at the foot of the Lincolnshire Wolds, Horncastle College offers a choice of more than 100 weekend, midweek and day courses on a wide range of topics, including history, music, astronomy, literature and a variety of arts and crafts.

For expert tuition, a friendly atmosphere, excellent food and comfortable accommodation in single or twin bedded rooms come to Horncastle, gateway to the Wolds.

Please send S.A.E. for programme to:

The Principal, Horncastle College, Mareham Road, Horncastle, Lincolnshire. LN9 6BW. Tel: 01507 522449, Fax: 01507 524382

162 October's autumn countryside £AFD

At the Misbourne School

163 China plate painting £AFD
164 Decorative painting £AFD
165 Portrait head sculpture £AFD
166 Practical opera weekend – *Carmen* £AFD
167 Make a sundial £AFD
168 Stained glass £AFD
169 Woodcarving: C&G and beyond £AFD
170 Home breadmaking with a master baker £AFD
171 Practical music workshop £AFD

Missenden Abbey, *Great Missenden*
ARCA

11–13 October

172 Calligraphy for Christmas £AFD
173 Lace making £AFD
174 Atmospheric watercolours £AFD
175 Map and compass for walkers £AFD

The Old Rectory, *Fittleworth*
ARCA

11–13 October

176 Découpage £AFD

Pendrell Hall College, *Codsall Wood*
ARCA

11–13 October

177 Archaeological illustration £AFD
178 Bath – variations on a theme £AFD
179 The reign of Edward II £AFD
180 Mushrooms or toadstools? £AFD

Univ Cambridge, *Madingley Hall*

11–13 October

181 Losing the thread £AFD
182 Painting fruits and fungi £AFD
183 Family history £AFD

Urchfont Manor College, *Devizes*
ARCA

11–13 October

184 Astronomy now £81

Wansfell College, *Theydon Bois*
ARCA

11–13 October

185 Customs of the waning year £184

Wensum Lodge, *Norwich*
ARCA

11–13 October

186 Repairing leather bindings £AFD
187 Shibori felt hats and accessories £AFD
188 Abstract and expression in drawing and painting £AFD

West Dean College, *Chichester*
ARCA

11–16 October

189 Stone sculpture workshop £AFD

West Dean College, *Chichester*
ARCA

11–18 October

190 Botanical illustration £253

Field Studies Council at Flatford Mill, *Colchester*

12–13 October

191 Art and multi craft weekend, with cane basket making, drawing and watercolour painting, flower arranging, calligraphy, patchwork and quilting £90
192 Fabric sculpture £70
193 Dressmaking £70
194 Machine embroidery £70
195 Bookbinding £82
196 Watercolours for beginners £82

Acorn Activities, *Herefordshire, Shropshire and Wales*

12–13 October
197 Portrait painting £22
198 Willow basket making – beginners £22
The Gateway, *Shrewsbury*
Local accommodation is arranged separately on request.

12–13 October
199 Rodin, women and the English connection £49*
Univ Manchester, *Manchester*
**Resident.*

12–18 October
200 Leisurely Lakeland rambles £AFD
Higham Hall, *Cockermouth*
ARCA

13–15 October
201 Turning frogs into princes – an intro to neuro-linguistic programming £76
Lancashire College, *Chorley*
ARCA

13–17 October
202 Router techniques and jig-making for cabinet makers £AFD
West Dean College, *Chichester*
ARCA

13–18 October
203 Fungi week £199
Field Studies Council at Flatford Mill, *Colchester*

13–18 October
204 Pottery general £AFD
205 Jewellery in silver £AFD
206 Life drawing £AFD
207 Atmospheric watercolours £AFD
West Dean College, *Chichester*
ARCA

14–16 October
208 Education in the nineteenth century £81
Wansfell College, *Theydon Bois*
ARCA

14–18 October
209 For the young at heart 50+ £110
Ammerdown Centre, *Radstock, Bath*

15–18 October
210 String chamber music £124*
Benslow Music Trust, *Hitchin*
ARCA
**Residential.*

16–23 October
211 Landscape painting in autumn £229
Field Studies Council at Nettlecombe Court, *Williton*

17–20 October
212 Country weekend with music £105
Beaconhill, *Deal, Kent*

18–20 October
213 Cider and wine tasting £195
Acorn Activities, *Herefordshire, Shropshire and Wales*

18–20 October
214 History of recorded sound £80
215 Enamelling for everyone £80
216 Drawing and painting flowers – the easy way £80
Alston Hall Residential College, *Preston*
ARCA

18–20 October
217 Bucks Point and Floral Torchon lace £95
218 Autumn fruits and flowers in line and wash £95
219 Celtic lettering £95
Belstead House, *Ipswich*
ARCA

18–20 October
220 String chamber music with piano £110*
Benslow Music Trust, *Hitchin*
ARCA
**Residential.*

18–20 October
221 Astronomy now £95
222 Improvers bridge £96
Burton Manor College, *South Wirral*
ARCA

18–20 October
223 William Morris £130*
224 Delight in books £115*
225 Social dreaming £115*
Dartington Hall, *Totnes, Devon*
***Residential.**

18–20 October
226 French £AFD
227 Silk painting £AFD
228 Writing your life story £AFD
Dillington House, *Ilminster*
ARCA

18–20 October
229 Landscapes of Exmoor £AFD
Dillington House, *Pinkery Centre, Minehead*
ARCA

18–20 October
230 Hedgelaying £98
231 Drawing buildings and landscapes £98
232 Family birdwatching £164*
233 Five more Suffolk villages £98
Field Studies Council at Flatford Mill, *Colchester*
****From £164 for 1 adult and 1 or 2 children.***

18–20 October
234 Castles and churches in the Marches £95
235 Fungal good £95
236 Photographing fungi £95
Field Studies Council at Preston Montford, *Shrewsbury*

18–20 October
237 Piano workshop £110
238 Silk painting for beginners £110
Higham Hall, *Cockermouth*
ARCA

18–20 October
239 Mediumship £84
The Hill Residential College, *Abergavenny*
ARCA

18–20 October
240 Creative lace £82
Horncastle College, *Horncastle*
ARCA

18–20 October
241 Yoga £87
242 Parchment craft for beginners £87
243 Canal boat art £87
244 Portrait painting £87
Knuston Hall, *Irchester*
ARCA

18–20 October
245 Surface and space – landscape and illusion £AFD
246 Drawing from observation using line and tone £AFD
247 Goldwork embroidery £AFD
248 ***I am the very model* – parodies in Gilbert and Sullivan** £AFD
249 Laugh and be well £AFD
250 Breaking the code – allegory in art and literature £AFD
251 Italian advanced £AFD
252 Thinkers for our times £AFD
Missenden Abbey, *Great Missenden*
ARCA

18–20 October
253 Painting detail in watercolour £AFD
254 Computers without consternation £AFD
255 Bach flower remedies £AFD
256 Strings workshop £AFD
The Old Rectory, *Fittleworth*
ARCA

18–20 October
257 Weekend for singers, teachers and conductors £85
Sing for Pleasure, *Wortley Hall, Sheffield*

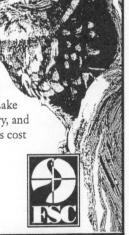

18–20 October
258 Embroiderers' guild £68–£86
Snowdonia National Park Centre, *Maentwrog*
ARCA

18–20 October
259 Fairy tales £AFD
260 Descartes 400 £AFD
261 Wagner's Ring: ***Siegfried*** £AFD
262 American art and literature of the Belle Epoch £AFD
Univ Cambridge, *Madingley Hall*

18–20 October
263 Computing: use of your home PC £110
264 The Vikings £90
Univ Nottingham, *Horncastle College, Lincs*

18–20 October
265 Fungi are fun £80
266 Pebbles on the beach £80
Univ Nottingham, *Gibraltar Point Field Centre*

18–20 October
267 Jane Austen and Bath £AFD
268 Mushrooms and toadstools £AFD
Urchfont Manor College, *Devizes*
ARCA

18–20 October
269 The Holy Land in Greek and Roman times £81
270 Make a skirt £81
Wansfell College, *Theydon Bois*
ARCA

18–20 October
271 New kingdom temples £184
Wensum Lodge, *Norwich*
ARCA

18–20 October
272 General silversmithing – emphasis on boxmaking £AFD
273 Getting started with watercolour £AFD
274 Calligraphy – back to basics £AFD
275 Gardening for wildlife £AFD
West Dean College, *Chichester*
ARCA

18–22 October
276 Getting the best from your camera £AFD
277 Woodturning for beginners and others £AFD
West Dean College, *Chichester*
ARCA

18–25 October
278 Stained glass £253
Field Studies Council at Flatford Mill, *Colchester*

18–25 October
279 The fascination of fungi £232
Field Studies Council at Preston Montford, *Shrewsbury*

19–20 October
280 Embroidery – shadow work £22
The Gateway, *Shrewsbury*
Local accommodation is arranged separately on request.

19–20 October
281 Introducing historic porcelain £50*
Univ Manchester, *Manchester*
****Resident.***

19–20 October
282 Down to earth: an introduction to geology £29*
Univ Oxford, *Oxford*
****Tuition fee. Accommodation and meals available.***

19–20 October
283 Contemporary history £36
284 Music £36
285 Philosophy £36
Wedgwood Memorial College, *Barlaston*
ARCA

20–25 October
286 Drawing and printmaking £196
287 Painting landscapes and still life £196
288 Autumn birds £199
Field Studies Council at Flatford Mill, ***Colchester***

20–25 October
289 Bridge for near beginners £AFD
Higham Hall, ***Cockermouth***
ARCA

20–25 October
290 Exploring Snowdonia's mountains £165–£210
291 Wildlife in autumn £165–£210
Snowdonia National Park Centre, ***Maentwrog***
ARCA

20–25 October
292 Botanical illustration – fruits and seeds £AFD
293 Autumn watercolours £AFD
West Dean College, ***Chichester***
ARCA

21–23 October
294 Workshop for singers £87
295 Festive needlecrafts £81
Wansfell College, ***Theydon Bois***
ARCA

21–24 October
296 Embroidery £165*
Dartington Hall, ***Totnes, Devon***
****Residential.***

21–24 October
297 French £118
298 Painting miniatures £118
299 Photography for beginners 118
The Hill Residential College, ***Abergavenny***
ARCA

21–24 October
300 Painting on silk £AFD
Urchfont Manor College, ***Devizes***
ARCA

21–25 October
301 Family wildlife week £450*
Field Studies Council at Juniper Hall, ***Dorking***
****For 2 adults accompanied by 1 or 2 children.***

21–25 October
302 Ford Castle: autumn study week £185*
Ford Castle, ***Berwick-upon-Tweed***
****Single room.***

21–25 October
303 Silk painting workshop £AFD
Higham Hall, ***Cockermouth***
ARCA

21–25 October
304 Paintings to be treasured £AFD
305 Walking and books £AFD
306 Clock repair £AFD
The Old Rectory, ***Fittleworth***
ARCA

21–25 October
307 Creative writing £128
Wedgwood Memorial College, ***Barlaston***
ARCA

23–25 October
308 Watercolours: painting trees £123
Acorn Activities, ***Herefordshire, Shropshire and Wales***

24–26 October
309 Nature in sugar craft £105
Field Studies Council at Dale Fort, ***Haverfordwest***

24–27 October
310 Walking weekend £105
Beaconhill, ***Deal, Kent***

24–27 October
311 Out and about £125
Field Studies Council at Nettlecombe Court, ***Williton***

25–27 October

- *312* Embroidered fabric covered boxes £80
- *313* Drawing for the terrified, part one £80

Alston Hall Residential College, ***Preston***
ARCA

25–27 October

- *314* Landscapes from photographs £95
- *315* Records ensembles £95

Belstead House, ***Ipswich***
ARCA

25–27 October

- *316* Wind chamber music £110*

Benslow Music Trust, ***Hitchin***
ARCA
****Residential.***

25–27 October

- *317* The divorce crisis £89
- *318* Creative writing £89

Braziers, ***Ipsden***
ARCA

25–27 October

- *319* Line dancing £AFD
- *320* The mines and quarries of Gwydyr £95*

Burton Manor College, ***South Wirral***
ARCA
****Plus transport.***

25–27 October

- *321* Arts and craft movement £AFD

Dillington House, ***Ilminster***
ARCA

25–27 October

- *322* Stained glass £95
- *323* Glorious garlands £95
- *324* Who was grandma's grandma? £95
- *325* Illustrating fungi £95
- *326* Battlefields of the Marches £105

Field Studies Council at Preston Montford, ***Shrewsbury***

25–27 October

- *327* Tai Ji £110
- *328* Fabric box making £110

Higham Hall, ***Cockermouth***
ARCA

25–27 October

- *329* Touching stillness £84
- *330* Advanced French 84
- *331* Magnificent buildings £84
- *332* Painting berries in autumn £84

The Hill Residential College, ***Abergavenny***
ARCA

25–27 October

- *333* Bridge £82
- *334* Picture framing £82
- *335* Painting and drawing £82

Horncastle College, ***Horncastle***
ARCA

25–27 October

- *336* Identification of lace £87
- *337* Decorative spicecraft £87
- *338* Hypnosis and relaxation £87
- *339* Folk weekend £87

Knuston Hall, ***Irchester***
ARCA

25–27 October

- *340* Spanish all levels £86
- *341* Gold thread embroidery £86

Lancashire College, ***Chorley***
ARCA

25–27 October

- *342* J. S. Bach – ***Magnificat* and *B Minor Mass*** £71–£99
- *343* Chinese brush paintings £71–£99

Maryland College, ***Woburn***
ARCA

25–27 October

- *344* Introduction to Welsh language £55

Meirionnydd Languages, ***North Wales***

25–27 October
345 Beethoven concertos £AFD
346 Early Picasso – Blue and Rose period £AFD
347 Figures on stumpwork embroidery £AFD
348 Teddy bears for collectors £AFD
349 Bead needle weaving for jewellery £AFD
350 The world of gemstones £AFD
351 Spanish advanced £AFD
352 Thatcherism and the new right £AFD
353 Writers' toolkit £AFD
354 Creating a magazine £AFD
Missenden Abbey, *Great Missenden*
ARCA

25–27 October
355 Stockmarket and investment for beginners £AFD
356 Singing for the tone deaf £AFD
357 Silverwork and jewellery £AFD
358 Watercolour landscapes £AFD
The Old Rectory, *Fittleworth*
ARCA

25–27 October
359 Music studies – Schubert £AFD
360 Autumn landscapes* £AFD
Pendrell Hall College, *Codsall Wood*
ARCA
****2 day non-residential.***

25–27 October
361 Battle of the Somme £AFD
362 The classical concerto £AFD
363 History of architecture: C20th £AFD
Univ Cambridge, *Madingley Hall*

25–27 October
364 Storm, flood and drought £95
Univ Nottingham, *Horncastle College, Lincs*

25–27 October
365 Piping workshop £AFD
366 Audio visual weekend £AFD
367 Cane and rush seating £AFD
Urchfont Manor College, *Devizes*
ARCA

25–27 October
368 American politics £81
369 German language through literature: intermediate 88
370 Machine knitting: cut and sew techniques £81
Wansfell College, *Theydon Bois*
ARCA

26–27 October
371 Records of medieval property £45*
Univ Oxford, *Oxford*
****Tuition fee. Accommodation and meals available.***

26–27 October
372 Women in literature £36
Wedgwood Memorial College, *Barlaston*
ARCA

27–29 October
373 Countryside in autumn £80
Alston Hall Residential College, *Preston*
ARCA

27–31 October
374 Sculptural ceramics £AFD
West Dean College, *Chichester*
ARCA

27 October–1 November
375 Improve your watercolours and pastels £196
Field Studies Council at Flatford Mill, *Colchester*

27 October–1 November
376 Beginners folk painting £AFD
Higham Hall, *Cockermouth*
ARCA

27 October–1 November
377 Cabinet making – part 2 £AFD
378 Gilding – part 1 £AFD
379 Fabric murals – appliqué and collage techniques for larger work £AFD
380 Observation and imagination – any medium £AFD
West Dean College, *Chichester*
ARCA

28–29 October
381 Tapestry weaving £26
The Gateway, *Shrewsbury*
Local accommodation is arranged separately on request.

28–30 October
382 The garden in autumn £95
Belstead House, *Ipswich*
ARCA

28–30 October
383 Crossroads of change £81
384 James Joyce: modern artist £81
Wansfell College, *Theydon Bois*
ARCA

28 October–1 November
385 The Stratford experience £235
Belstead House, *Ipswich and Stratford-on-Avon*
ARCA

28 October–1 November
386 Paris, pastels and Margaret Glass £AFD
Belstead House, *Ipswich and Paris*
ARCA

29–31 October
387 Practical lace £89
Horncastle College, *Horncastle*
ARCA

29 October–1 November
388 Bridge – defensive bidding and defensive play £155–£160
Hawthorn Bridge, *Eastbourne, Sussex*

30 October–1 November
389 Starting to paint £95
Burton Manor College, *South Wirral*
ARCA

30 October–1 November
390 Parchment craft £81
Wansfell College, *Theydon Bois*
ARCA

■ ■ ■ ■

November 1996

□ □ □ □

1–3 November
391 Floral craft – Christmas arrangements £80
Alston Hall Residential College, *Preston*
ARCA

1–3 November
392 Go-it-alone lace £76
393 Patchwork and quilting £95
Belstead House, *Ipwich*
ARCA

1–3 November
394 Jazz plus strings £110*
395 Alexander Technique for pianists £110*
396 Introduction to watercolour painting £105*
Benslow Music Trust, *Hitchin*
ARCA
****Residential.***

1–3 November
397 Relax at Braziers in winter £89

398 The tao of management £89
Braziers, *Ipsden*
ARCA

1–3 November
399 Writers' dream workshop £95
400 Garden design £95
401 Introduction to aromatherapy £95
Burton Manor College, *South Wirral*
ARCA

1–3 November
402 Brahms' chamber music £AFD
403 Knights Templers £AFD
Dillington House, *Ilminster*
ARCA

1–3 November
404 Painting in oils and acrylics £98
405 Improve your pastel painting £98
406 Hedgelaying £98
Field Studies Council at Flatford Mill, *Colchester*

1–3 November
407 Karate £84
408 Basic picture framing £84
409 Christmas photography £84
410 Writers' workshop £84
The Hill Residential College, *Abergavenny*
ARCA

1–3 November
411 Return to learn £82
412 Landscapes of the body £82
413 Family history for beginners £82
414 Cross stitch for beginners £82
Horncastle College, *Horncastle*
ARCA

1–3 November
415 Cities of Vesuvius £87
416 Lacemaking for all £87
417 Lingerie and blouses £87
Knuston Hall, *Irchester*
ARCA

1–3 November
418 French all levels £86
419 The Celestine Prophecy £86
Lancashire College, *Chorley*
ARCA

1–3 November
420 Portrait painting £71–£99
421 Alexander Technique £71–£99
Maryland College, *Woburn*
ARCA

1–3 November
422 French conversation £55
Meirionnydd Languages, *North Wales*

1–3 November
423 The legend of Don Juan £AFD
424 Miniature painting – beginners and improvers £AFD
425 Jazzed-up jerseys £AFD
426 Honiton lace £AFD
427 Visual arts – 1860–1880 £AFD
428 Politics and power in Regency England £AFD
429 Post-superwoman – getting your life in balance £AFD
Missenden Abbey, *Great Missenden*
ARCA

1–3 November
430 Wet in wet £AFD
431 Recorder weekend £AFD
432 Chess £AFD
433 Christmas decorations £AFD
The Old Rectory, *Fittleworth*
ARCA

1–3 November
434 Chinese brush painting £AFD
435 Recorder playing £AFD
Pendrell Hall College, *Codsall Wood*
ARCA

1–3 November
436 Children's singing weekend £50*
Sing for Pleasure, *Quorn, Leicester*
****£40 per child.***

1–3 November
437 Shakespeare: from page to stage £199
Univ Birmingham, *Stratford-upon-Avon*

1–3 November
438 Reading classical Greek: advanced £AFD
439 Spanish art from El Greco to Picasso and Dali £AFD
Univ Cambridge, *Madingley Hall*

1–3 November
440 Opera North weekend £AFD
Univ Nottingham, *Nottingham*

1–3 November
441 Birds in winter £80
Univ Nottingham, *Gibraltar Point, Lincs*

1–3 November
442 Late Anglo-Saxon towns £42*
Univ Oxford, *Oxford*
Tuition fee. Accommodation and meals available.

1–3 November
443 The development of detective stories £AFD
444 Calligraphy for Christmas £AFD
Urchfont Manor College, *Devizes*
ARCA

1–3 November
445 Federation of worker writers £65
Wedgwood Memorial College, *Barlaston*
ARCA

1–3 November
446 Playing jazz £184
447 Basic introduction to psychology £184
Wensum Lodge, *Norwich*
ARCA

1–3 November
448 Woodturning for beginners £AFD
449 Terracotta modelling – horses and animals £AFD
450 Loose covers for chairs – part I £AFD
451 Beaded bags and tassels £AFD
452 Basic blacksmithing £AFD
453 Opera and recital – masterclasses for advanced singers and pianists £AFD
West Dean College, *Chichester*
ARCA

1–4 November
454 Mosaics in marble, glass and stone £AFD
West Dean College, *Chichester*
ARCA

1–30 November
455 Basket making with cane £35*
456 Sugarcraft £35*
457 Eggcraft £35*
458 Flower arranging £35*
459 Bonsai £35*
460 Fabric sculpture £35*
461 Decorative interiors and paintwork £35*
462 Stencilling £35*
463 Needlecraft £35*
464 Strawcraft £35*
465 Machine knitting £35*
466 Patchwork and quilting £35*
467 Découpage – 3D £35*
468 Découpage – traditional £35*
469 Drawing, watercolours and oils £35*
470 Gardening skills £35*
471 Rush seating £35*
472 Cane seating £35*
473 Pottery – any Thursday £35*
474 Music – any instrument 2 hours £35*
475 Languages – one hour £15*
476 Birdwatching £40*
477 Furniture restoration – any 2 consecutive days £100
478 Woodwork – any 3 consecutive days £150
Acorn Activities, *Herefordshire, Shropshire and Wales*
Per day. Bookings can be made for any number of days.

2–3 November
479 Victorian applique on glass £70
480 Drawing and painting: animals and landscapes £82
481 Pottery £70
Acorn Activities, *Herefordshire, Shropshire and Wales*

2–3 November
482 Clay portrait modelling £22
483 Greetings cards – personalised £21
484 Picture framing £26
485 Stained glass £44
The Gateway, *Shrewsbury*
Local accommodation is arranged separately on request.

2–7 November
486 Moods of the mountains £165–£210
Snowdonia National Park Centre, *Maentwrog*
ARCA

3–5 November
487 Hypnotherapy and psychotherapy £76
Lancashire College, *Chorley*
ARCA

3–6 November
488 Decorative painting on furniture £AFD
West Dean College, *Chichester*
ARCA

3–8 November
489 Intro to watercolour painting £AFD
Higham Hall, *Cockermouth*
ARCA

3–8 November
490 Portrait painting and drawing – all media £AFD
491 Decorative tassels, cords and woven braids £AFD
492 Watercolour – intermediate £AFD
West Dean College, *Chichester*
ARCA

4–6 November
493 Retired citizens course £AFD
Pendrell Hall College, *Staffs*
ARCA

4–6 November
494 Alexander Technique £81
Wansfell College, *Theydon Bois*
ARCA

4–7 November
495 Book binding £AFD
Urchfont Manor College, *Devizes*
ARCA

4–8 November
496 Modern pencil drawing £AFD
497 Stencilling and printing £AFD
498 China painting £AFD
The Old Rectory, *Fittleworth*
ARCA

5–7 November
499 Aromatherapy £76
Lancashire College, *Chorley*
ARCA

6–13 November
500 Fossils of Pembrokeshire £245
Field Studies Council at Dale Fort, *Haverfordwest*

7–10 November
501 International conference: the psychology of awakening – Buddhism, science and psychotherapy £210*
Dartington Hall, *Totnes, Devon*
****Plus accommodation and concert.***

7–10 November
502 Sign communication skills stage II module I £AFD
Lancashire College, *Chorley*
ARCA

8–10 November
503 Bridge weekend £125
Acorn Activities, *Herefordshire, Shropshire and Wales*

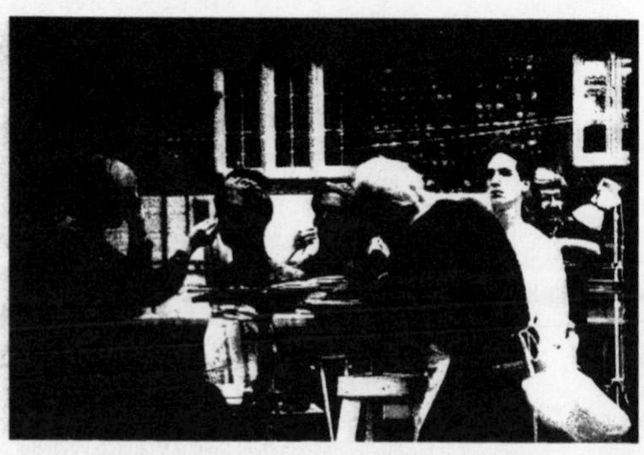

8–10 November
504 Bedfordshire lacemaking £80
505 Recorder playing workshop £80
506 Painting in watercolours £80
Alston Hall Residential College, *Preston*
ARCA

8–10 November
507 Viol consorts £110*
508 Piano class II £105*
509 Preparing for grade 5 theory £105*
Benslow Music Trust, *Hitchin*
ARCA
****Residential.***

8–10 November
510 Myths and legends £95
Burton Manor College, *South Wirral*
ARCA

8–10 November
511 Dutch 17th century painters £AFD
Dillington House, *Ilminster*
ARCA

8–10 November
512 Batik and silk painting £98
513 Watercolour – beginners £98
514 Painting plants: autumn colours and designs £98
Field Studies Council at Flatford Mill, *Colchester*

8–10 November
515 The world of the microscope £260*
Field Studies Council at Juniper Hall, *Dorking*
****For 2 adults accompanied by 1 or 2 children.***

8–10 November
516 The nuclear debate £110
517 Story of Scandinavia £110
518 Drawing £110
Higham Hall, *Cockermouth*
ARCA

8–10 November
519 Bridge for improvers £87
520 Chinese brush painting £87
521 Your total image £87
522 Italian literature £87
Knuston Hall, *Irchester*
ARCA

8–10 November
523 German all levels £86
Lancashire College, *Chorley*
ARCA

8–10 November
524 The Renaissance courts of central Italy £71–£99
Maryland College, *Woburn*
ARCA

8–10 November
525 ***Lohengrin*** **– Wagner's last opera** £AFD
526 Learn to paint with watercolour £AFD
527 C&G embroidery part 1 year 2 £AFD
528 C&G patchwork and quilting £AFD
529 Napoleon and Josephine £AFD
530 Write on – skills for publication £AFD
531 French literature £AFD
532 Flowermaking for millinery £AFD
At the Misbourne School
533 Middle Eastern folk dance £AFD
534 Family and community history £AFD
535 Wire, wood and papier maché £AFD
536 Getting started on design £AFD
537 Silk painting workshop £AFD
538 Making miniature furniture £AFD
539 Celtic knot designs £AFD
Missenden Abbey, *Great Missenden*
ARCA

8–10 November
540 Natural history illustration £AFD
541 Write a short, short story £AFD
542 Computer textile design £AFD
543 Decorative paint effects £AFD
The Old Rectory, *Fittleworth*
ARCA

8–10 November
544 Yoga in Snowdonia £68–£86
Snowdonia National Park Centre, *Maentwrog*
ARCA

8–10 November
545 Practical astronomy workshop £AFD
546 Later C20th writing: the interface and developments £AFD
547 Spanish weekend £AFD
548 Eminent Edwardians £AFD
Univ Cambridge, *Madingley Hall*

8–10 November
549 Europe in the Enlightenment (A206) £AFD
Urchfont Manor College, *Devizes*
ARCA

8–10 November
550 Astronomy now £AFD
551 Canal boat art: a practical course £81
Wansfell College, *Theydon Bois*
ARCA

8–10 November
552 Printmaking workshop – relief colour printing £AFD
553 Batik workshop £AFD
554 Glass engraving £AFD
555 Life painting in watercolours £AFD
556 Signwriting and brush lettering £AFD
557 Travel journalism £AFD
West Dean College, *Chichester*
ARCA

8–11 November
558 Creative hand embroidery from nature £105
Field Studies Council at Dale Fort, *Haverfordwest*

8–11 November
559 Creative black and white photography £AFD
West Dean College, *Chichester*
ARCA

9–10 November
560 Israel and the Holy Land £26
561 Kitemaking for the family £22
562 Life weekend – beginners £27
563 Writing fiction £19
The Gateway, *Shrewsbury*
Local accommodation is arranged separately on request.

9–10 November
564 The string quartet: a performer's perspective £AFD
Univ Manchester, *Manchester*

9–10 November
565 Intermediate German language £65
Wedgwood Memorial College, *Barlaston*
ARCA

10–13 November
566 China painting for sheer enjoyment £131
Alston Hall Residential College, *Preston*
ARCA

10–15 November
567 Cut, sew and decorate machine knitted garments £200
Alston Hall Residential College, *Preston*
ARCA

10–15 November
568 Bookbinding £196
Field Studies Council at Flatford Mill, *Colchester*

10–15 November
569 Autumn pastel painting £AFD
Higham Hall, *Cockermouth*
ARCA

10–16 November
570 Beginners Russian £125
Meirionnydd Languages, *North Wales*

11–14 November
571 Foundation course for strings £135*
Benslow Music Trust, *Hitchin*
ARCA
****Residential.***

11–14 November
572 Back to natural fibre £105
Field Studies Council at Dale Fort, *Haverfordwest*

13–15 November
573 Alexander Technique – an introduction £83
Alston Hall Residential College, *Preston*
ARCA

15–17 November
574 Scrabble weekend £125
575 Murder, mystery weekend £195
Acorn Activities, *Herefordshire, Shropshire and Wales*

15–17 November
576 Gold thread embroidery £80
Alston Hall Residential College, *Preston*
ARCA

15–17 November
577 Découpage: three dimensional papercraft £67*
578 Porcelain gifts for Christmas £67*
579 Circle dance £67
Ammerdown Centre, *Radstock, Bath*
****Plus equipment.***

15–17 November
580 Crafts for Christmas £95
Belstead House, *Ipswich*
ARCA

15–17 November
581 Advanced quartets £140*
Benslow Music Trust, *Hitchin*
ARCA
****Residential.***

15–17 November
582 Christmas allsorts £95
583 Wine and Spirit Education Trust Certificate £95
584 Memoir writing £95
585 Colour negative printing £155
Burton Manor College, *South Wirral*
ARCA

15–17 November
586 Old age and dying £125*
587 French language and culture £115*
588 Calligraphy £110*
Dartington Hall, *Totnes, Devon*
****Residential.***

15–17 November
589 Calligraphy £AFD
Dillington House, *Ilminster*
ARCA

15–17 November
590 Geology £95
591 Tranquil Lakeland £95
592 Introduction to black and white photography £95
Field Studies Council at Blencathra, *Keswick*

15–17 November
593 Chinese brush painting £90/£98
Hawkwood College, *Stroud*
ARCA

15–17 November
594 Schubert's last year £110
595 Intro to garden design £110
596 Advanced mushroom hunting £110
Higham Hall, *Cockermouth*
ARCA

15–17 November
597 Welsh £84
598 Lace £84
The Hill Residential College, *Abergavenny*
ARCA

15–17 November
599 Calligraphy and colour £82
600 Yoga for stress release £82
Horncastle College, *Horncastle*
ARCA

15–17 November
601 Traditional upholstery skills £87
Knuston Hall, *Irchester*
ARCA

15–17 November
602 Découpage £86
603 Flower painting in watercolour £86
604 Assertiveness training £86
605 Tai Chi Chuan £86
Lancashire College, *Chorley*
ARCA

15–17 November
606 Lacemaking £71–£99
607 Advanced French £71–£99
Maryland College, *Woburn*
ARCA

15–17 November
608 Granada – world of Lorca and de Falla £AFD
609 Analytical drawing and perspective £AFD
610 C&G basketry – plaited baskets £AFD
611 Fabric Christmas decorations and ornaments £AFD
612 Preparing working designs £AFD
613 Cours de Français intermédiaire £AFD
614 Drinking and the English: a history of the public house £AFD
615 German – intermediate £AFD
616 Reflexology £AFD
Missenden Abbey, *Great Missenden*
ARCA

15–17 November
617 How to draw up a family tree £AFD
618 Have fun with your sketch book £AFD
619 Great Nordic composers £AFD
620 Gifts to make £AFD
The Old Rectory, *Fittleworth*
ARCA

15–17 November
621 Gwneud Dillad £68–£86
622 Sampleri Cymraeg £68–£86
Snowdonia National Park Centre, *Maentwrog*
ARCA

15–17 November
623 Plato's Theaetetus £AFD
624 The architecture of death £AFD
625 The Pacific War £AFD
626 Benjamin Britten and Michael Tippett £AFD
Univ Cambridge, *Madingley Hall*

15–17 November
627 Safari: big game and big money £90
628 Countryside in winter £95
Univ Nottingham, *Horncastle College, Lincs*

15–17 November
629 The language of art £AFD
630 Meditation to quieten the mind £AFD
Urchfont Manor College, *Devizes*
ARCA

15–17 November
631 Scottish Gaelic £81
Wansfell College, *Theydon Bois*
ARCA

15–17 November
632 Cabinet making – part 1 £AFD
633 Mounting and framing pictures £AFD
634 Pottery – throwing and turning with handle-making £AFD
635 Botanical illustration £AFD
636 Lace-making in miniature and textiles for dolls and dolls houses £AFD
637 Silversmithing – making hammers for precious metal working £AFD
West Dean College, *Chichester*
ARCA

15–18 November
638 Music appreciation – *Die Meistersinger* – Wagner £120
Alston Hall Residential College, *Preston*
ARCA

15–18 November
639 Winter environmental break £105
Field Studies Council at Dale Fort, *Haverfordwest*

16–17 November
640 Gourmet cooking £100
641 Bridge for beginners £75
Acorn Activities, *Herefordshire, Shropshire and Wales*

16–17 November
642 William and Mary £49*
643 Voice journeys £60*
Univ Manchester, *Manchester*
Resident.

16–17 November
644 The human skeleton in archaeology £45*
Univ Oxford, *Oxford*
Tuition fee. Accommodation and meals available.

16–17 November
645 Contemporary history £36
646 Music £36
647 Philosophy £36
Wedgwood Memorial College, *Barlaston*
ARCA

17–22 November
648 Winter birds of sea, estuary and coast £185
649 Mountain leader training £274
Field Studies Council at Rhyd-y-creuau, *Betws-y-coed*

17–22 November
650 Photography at year's end £165–£210
Snowdonia National Park Centre, *Maentwrog*
ARCA

17–22 November
651 Repairing and refinishing antique furniture £AFD
652 General silversmithing £AFD
653 A seasonal sketchbook – mixed media £AFD
654 Lampshades – tailored, lined and hand-pleated £AFD
West Dean College, *Chichester*
ARCA

18–20 November
655 Humour and romance in Jane Austen £81
Wansfell College, *Theydon Bois*
ARCA

18–22 November
656 Bookcraft £AFD
657 Painting in oils £AFD
658 Poetry for winter £AFD
The Old Rectory, *Fittleworth*
ARCA

20–22 November
659 Line and wash £AFD
Urchfont Manor College, *Devizes*
ARCA

22–24 November
660 Bridge weekend £125
Acorn Activities, *Herefordshire, Shropshire and Wales*

22–24 November
661 Chamber music for string quartets £83
Alston Hall Residential College, *Preston*
ARCA

22–24 November
662 Renaissance band £110*
663 Choose your piece for cello £110*
Benslow Music Trust, *Hitchin*
ARCA
Residential.

22–24 November
664 Crystal healing £AFD
Burton Manor College, *South Wirral*
ARCA

22–24 November
665 Choral weekend: Mendelssohn's *Elijah* £120*
Dartington Hall, *Totnes, Devon*
Residential.

22–24 November
666 Darkroom photography £AFD
667 Cut and sew £AFD
Dillington House, *Ilminster*
ARCA

22–24 November
668 Chinese brush painting £98
669 Small mammal weekend £98
670 East Anglian steam railways £98
Field Studies Council at Flatford Mill, *Colchester*

22–24 November
671 Bridge – accurate bidding: modern acol £130/£138
Hawthorn Bridge, *Alfriston, Sussex*

22–24 November
672 Shakespeare's festive comedy £110
673 Christmas patchwork £110
Higham Hall, *Cockermouth*
ARCA

22–24 November
674 European novel £84
675 Spanish £84
676 Clay modelling £84
677 Advanced bridge £84
678 Landscape in watercolour £84
679 Metal thread embroidery £84
The Hill Residential College, *Abergavenny*
ARCA

22–24 November
680 China painting £82
681 Decorative finishes £82
682 English and continental lace £82
683 Celebrating in dance and song £82
Horncastle College, *Horncastle*
ARCA

22–24 November
684 Natural tied flowers (for gifts and weddings) £87
685 Creative embroidery for Christmas gifts and decorations £87
686 Beauty and art: the Greeks £AFD
Knuston Hall, *Irchester*
ARCA

22–24 November
687 Miniature furniture for dolls' houses £86
688 Wine appreciation £86
689 Yoga £86
690 Creative writing £86
Lancashire College, *Chorley*
ARCA

22–24 November
691 The Romanovs – a family portrait £71–£99
692 The history of glass in northern Europe £81–£109
Maryland College, *Woburn*
ARCA

22–24 November
693 Tai Ji – active relaxation £AFD
694 Watercolour techniques for improvers £AFD
695 C&G embroidery part 2 year 2 £AFD
696 C&G embroidery part 2 year 1 £AFD
697 The route to St James of Compostela £AFD
698 Portuguese – intermediate £AFD
699 The popular novel £AFD
700 Anyone can read music – part 1 £AFD
Missenden Abbey, *Great Missenden*
ARCA

22–24 November
701 Woodcarving £AFD
702 The beguiling medium (watercolour) £AFD
703 Harpsichord workshop £AFD
The Old Rectory, *Fittleworth*
ARCA

22–24 November
704 Russian weekend £AFD
705 Reading Latin £AFD
706 The early Anglo Saxon kingdom of East Anglia £AFD
707 Filming fiction £AFD
Univ Cambridge, *Madingley Hall*

22–24 November
708 The prelude and first night of Wagner's ***Ring Cycle*** £98*
Univ Manchester, *Manchester*
**Resident.*

22–24 November
709 The seigneurial residence in Europe £42*
Univ Oxford, *Oxford*
**Tuition fee. Accommodation and meals available.*

22–24 November
710 Astronomy for beginners £AFD
Urchfont Manor College, *Devizes*
ARCA

22–24 November
711 German language through literature: advanced £89
712 Oriental carpets (The Oriental Rug and Textile Society of Great Britain) £81
713 Photography: introduction to colour printing £98
Wansfell College, *Theydon Bois*
ARCA

22–24 November
714 Introduction to woodturning £AFD
715 Traditional upholstery for beginners £AFD
716 Boxmaking, smallwork, lathe and punch techniques £AFD
717 Making miniature furniture – stage I £AFD
718 Still life with flowers £AFD
719 Passementerie – tasselmaking from jute £AFD
720 Watercolour painting for beginners £AFD
West Dean College, *Chichester*
ARCA

22–29 November
721 Portrait painting £269
Field Studies Council at Flatford Mill, *Colchester*

23–24 November
722 Calligraphy – a brush with coloured capitals £22
723 Have I got news for you? £20
724 Rag dolls and gollies £24
725 Watercolour painting £20
The Gateway, *Shrewsbury*
Local accommodation is arranged separately on request.

23–24 November
726 Women in literature £36
Wedgwood Memorial College, *Barlaston*
ARCA

24–27 November
727 Handmade papers from plants £AFD
West Dean College, *Chichester*
ARCA

24–29 November
728 Computer aided knitwear design £200
Alston Hall Residential College, *Preston*
ARCA

24–29 November
729 Stained glass: a beginners' course £196
730 Botanical painting £196
731 Picture framing £196
Field Studies Council at Flatford Mill, *Colchester*

24–29 November
732 Stained glass workshop £AFD
Higham Hall, *Cockermouth*
ARCA

24–29 November
733 Painting £165–£210
Snowdonia National Park Centre, *Maentwrog*
ARCA

24–29 November
734 Woodturning – advanced £AFD
735 Shipwrights' workshop – boat repair – traditional techniques £AFD
736 Loose covers for chairs – part 2 £AFD
West Dean College, *Chichester*
ARCA

24–30 November
737 Beginners Welsh £125
Meirionnydd Languages, *North Wales*

25–27 November
738 Discovering geology £81
Wansfell College, *Theydon Bois*
ARCA

27–29 November
739 Developing your potential £AFD
Pendrell Hall College, *Codsall Wood*
ARCA

28 November–1 December
740 Sign communication skills stage III module I £AFD
Lancashire College, *Chorley*
ARCA

29 November–1 December
741 Ruskin lacemaking £80
742 The eight limbs of yoga £80
Alston Hall Residential College, *Preston*
ARCA

29 November–1 December
743 Dig where you stand – writing £95
744 City states of central Italy £95
Belstead House, *Ipswich*
ARCA

29 November–1 December
745 Early music singing £110*
746 Classical piano £105*
Benslow Music Trust, *Hitchin*
ARCA
Residential.

29 November–1 December
747 Folklore in England £89
748 Reflexology and aromatherapy £89
Braziers, *Ipsden*
ARCA

29 November–1 December
749 Noel Coward £95
750 Goldwork embroidery £95
Burton Manor College, *South Wirral*
ARCA

29 November–1 December
751 Bridge £AFD
Dillington House, *Ilminster*
ARCA

29 November–1 December
752 Enamelling: a beginners' course £98
753 Late autumn bird weekend £98
754 Improve your photography: black-and-white printing £98
Field Studies Council at Flatford Mill, *Colchester*

29 November–1 December
755 Archaeology of the Orkneys – part two £110
756 Cake icing £110
Higham Hall, *Cockermouth*
ARCA

29 November–1 December
757 Shaping of modern Spain £84
758 Découpage £84
759 Adventures in pen and ink £84
The Hill Residential College, *Abergavenny*
ARCA

29 November–1 December
760 French intermediate/upper £87
761 Benito Perez Galdos £87
762 Wind band £87
Knuston Hall, *Irchester*
ARCA

29 November–1 December
763 Stained glass £86
764 Calligraphy £86
Lancashire College, *Chorley*
ARCA

29 November–1 December
765 Israel and the Holy Land £71–£99
766 Fanny Burney £71–£99
Maryland College, *Woburn*
ARCA

29 November–1 December
767 Masters of macabre – art and music £AFD
768 Passementerie – BOCN £AFD
769 C&G interior design £AFD
770 Winter wines from warm climates £AFD
771 Bridge – modern acol bidding £AFD
772 Improve figure drawing £AFD
773 Professional people working from home £AFD
Missenden Abbey, *Great Missenden*
ARCA

29 November–1 December
774 Winter landscapes of Fittleworth £AFD
775 Countdown to Christmas £AFD
776 Handbells in harmony £AFD
The Old Rectory, *Fittleworth*
ARCA

29 November–1 December
777 Cross stitch weekend £68–£86
Snowdonia National Park Centre, *Maentwrog*
ARCA

29 November–1 December
778 French weekend £AFD
779 Reading classical Greek £AFD
780 Landscapes of the mind £AFD
781 Visconti and the German dream £AFD
Univ Cambridge, *Madingley Hall*

29 November–1 December
782 *The Ring* continued. *Siegfried and Gotterdammerung* (Twilight of the Gods) £98*
Univ Manchester, *Manchester*
****Resident.***

29 November–1 December
783 Geology: brush up your igneous rocks £AFD
784 Calligraphy – decorative pen letters £AFD
Urchfont Manor College, *Devizes*
ARCA

29 November–1 December
785 Glass engraving – stipple and line techniques £AFD
786 Life drawing £AFD
787 Painting miniatures and silhouettes £AFD
788 Basic blacksmithing £AFD
789 Viol consort music £AFD
West Dean College, *Chichester*
ARCA

29 November–3 December
790 Decorative and marbled papers £AFD
791 Silk painting – new techniques including velvet £AFD
West Dean College, *Chichester*
ARCA

29 November–4 December
792 Improve your photography: black-and-white printing £196
793 Researching and writing local history £196
Field Studies Council at Flatford Mill, *Colchester*

30 November–1 December

794 Painting £25
795 Screen printing techniques – developing £22

The Gateway, *Shrewsbury*
Local accommodation is arranged separately on request.

30 November–1 December

796 Collectors great and small: art in Oxford £29*

Univ Oxford, *Oxford*
**Tuition fee. Accommodation and meals available.*

■ ■ ■ ■

December 1996

□ □ □ □

1–5 December

797 Machine embroidery – colour your gold £AFD

West Dean College, *Chichester*
ARCA

1–6 December

798 Autumn watercolours £AFD
799 Blacksmithing and wrought ironwork £AFD
800 Black and white printing to exhibition standard £AFD

West Dean College, *Chichester*
ARCA

1–31 December

801 Basket making with cane £35*
802 Sugarcraft £35*
803 Eggcraft £35*
804 Flower arranging £35*
805 Bonsai £35*
806 Fabric sculpture £35*
807 Decorative interiors and paintwork £35*
808 Stencilling £35*
809 Needlecraft £35*
810 Strawcraft £35*
811 Machine knitting £35*
812 Patchwork and quilting £35*
813 Découpage – 3D £35*
814 Découpage – traditional £35*
815 Drawing, watercolours and oils £35*
816 Gardening skills £35*
817 Rush seating £35*
818 Cane seating £35*
819 Pottery – any Thursday £35*
820 Music – any instrument 2 hours £35*
821 Languages – one hour £15*
822 Birdwatching £40*
823 Furniture restoration – any 2 consecutive days £100
824 Woodwork – any 3 consecutive days £150

Acorn Activities, *Herefordshire, Shropshire and Wales*
****Per day. Bookings can be made for any number of days.***

2–4 December

825 Bobbin lacemaking £81
826 East End music hall £91

Wansfell College, *Theydon Bois*
ARCA

2–6 December

827 Mountain leader assessment £274

Field Studies Council at Rhyd-y-creuau, *Betws-y-coed*

2–6 December

828 Painting the seasons £AFD
829 Christmas singing workshop £AFD
830 Ceramic restoration £AFD

The Old Rectory, *Fittleworth*
ARCA

2–6 December
831 The inside out – painting course £130
Wedgwood Memorial College, ***Barlaston***
ARCA

4–8 December
832 Alexander Technique – follow up £89
Alston Hall Residential College, ***Preston***
ARCA

5–8 December
833 Silversmithing £118
The Hill Residential College, ***Abergavenny***
ARCA

6–8 December
834 The Victorian family £80
835 Life drawing – an introduction £80
Alston Hall Residential College, ***Preston***
ARCA

6–8 December
836 Folk for fun £95
Belstead House, ***Ipswich***
ARCA

6–8 December
837 String chamber music £105*
Benslow Music Trust, ***Hitchin***
ARCA
****Residential.***

6–8 December
838 Wine and Spirit Education Trust Certificate £95
Burton Manor College, ***South Wirral***
ARCA

6–8 December
839 The Bible and Ancient Egypt £AFD
840 Philosophy, evolution and ethics £AFD
Dillington House, ***Ilminster***
ARCA

6–8 December
841 War studies – border battles £110
842 Wood carving £110
Higham Hall, ***Cockermouth***
ARCA

6–8 December
843 Astrology £84
844 Healing hands £84
845 Aromatherapy £84
846 Medieval art and architecture £84
The Hill Residential College, ***Abergavenny***
ARCA

6–8 December
847 Creative lace £82
848 Head sculpture £82
849 Feeling good about yourself and others £82
Horncastle College, ***Horncastle***
ARCA

6–8 December
850 Reflexology £87
Knuston Hall, ***Irchester***
ARCA

6–8 December
851 Christmas international – French/German/Spanish – elementary, Greek all levels £86
Lancashire College, ***Chorley***
ARCA

6–8 December
852 Handel – the operas £71–£99
853 French literature – *L'enfant et les Grandes Personnes* £71–£99
Maryland College, ***Woburn***
ARCA

6–8 December
854 Handmade teddy bears £55
Meirionnydd Languages, ***North Wales***

6–8 December
855 Great collections £AFD
856 Painting watercolour landscapes from photographs £AFD
857 Project general drawing £AFD
858 Machine embroidery £AFD
859 French gangster film £AFD
860 The global food system £AFD
861 Poetry writers' workshop £AFD
At the Misbourne School
862 The creative self £AFD
863 Embroidered caskets £AFD
864 Drama – acting truth and passion £AFD
865 Traditional and modern upholstery £AFD
866 Picture framing £AFD
867 Crochet in colour £AFD
868 Working freely with clay £AFD
869 Woodcarving C&G and beyond £AFD
870 Sugarcraft – not another snow scene £AFD
Missenden Abbey, *Great Missenden*
ARCA

6–8 December
871 Stained glass workshop £AFD
872 An introduction to astronomy £AFD
873 Make a collector's teddy bear £AFD
874 Pastel workshop £AFD
The Old Rectory, *Fittleworth*
ARCA

6–8 December
875 Advanced bridge £AFD
876 Early music £AFD
Pendrell Hall College, *Codsall Wood*
ARCA

6–8 December
877 Christmas and midwinter: custom and ritual in England 1600–1914 £148
Univ Birmingham, *Bromsgrove*

6–8 December
878 Romanesque France: art and architecture £AFD
879 Pascal £AFD
880 British Intelligence successes £AFD
Univ Cambridge, *Madingley Hall*

6–8 December
881 Fifty years of French music 1870–1920 £AFD
882 Cords and tassels £AFD
Urchfont Manor College, *Devizes*
ARCA

6–8 December
883 America in the 1920s and 1930s £81
884 Workshop for singers £87
885 Two linked French courses – advanced £87
Wansfell College, *Theydon Bois*
ARCA

6–8 December
886 Repairing and refinishing antique furniture £AFD
887 Bangles and spoons – working in silver £AFD
888 Watercolour for beginners £AFD
889 Calligraphy for beginners £AFD
890 Developing a winter colour palette £AFD
891 Master potter series: 5 £AFD
West Dean College, *Chichester*
ARCA

7–8 December
892 Festive decorations for the Christmas season £70
893 Pottery £70
Acorn Activities, *Herefordshire, Shropshire and Wales*

8–11 December
894 Silk painting £AFD
895 Low relief and chip carving in wood £AFD
West Dean College, *Chichester*
ARCA

8–13 December
896 Creative drawing with colour £AFD
West Dean College, *Chichester*
ARCA

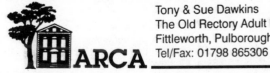

10–11 December
897 Fun with dyes £26
The Gateway, *Shrewsbury*
Local accommodation is arranged separately on request.

10–12 December
898 China painting £AFD
Pendrell Hall College, *Staffs*
ARCA

11–13 December
899 Portrait painting £107
Burton Manor College, *South Wirral*
ARCA

13–15 December
900 Painting in oils £85
901 Calligraphy £80
Alston Hall Residential College, *Preston*
ARCA

13–15 December
902 Line dancing £AFD
903 Black and white printing £155
Burton Manor College, *South Wirral*
ARCA

13–15 December
904 Houseparty £AFD
Dillington House, *Ilminster*
ARCA

13–15 December
905 Yoga £84
906 Talking with confidence £84
907 Wine £84
908 Rambling £84
The Hill Residential College, *Abergavenny*
ARCA

13–15 December
909 Fabric Christmas decorations and cards £87
910 Flower painting £87
911 Wines of Bordeaux and Burgundy £112
912 Early music singing £89
Knuston Hall, *Irchester*
ARCA

13–15 December
913 Christmas international – Spanish/German/French/Italian intermediate/advanced £86
Lancashire College, *Chorley*
ARCA

13–15 December
914 Shakespeare's kings £71–£99
915 Exploring the Cecil Higgins museum £77–£105
Maryland College, *Woburn*
ARCA

13–15 December
916 Random patchwork £55
Meirionnydd Languages, *North Wales*

13–15 December
917 Decadence and symbolism in art and music £AFD
918 Dangerous drawing £AFD
919 Bags of beads £AFD
920 Life drawing and painting – ref: Degas £AFD
921 Temari balls and rice dumplings £AFD
922 A Dickensian Christmas £AFD
923 Dramatists who wrote alongside Shakespeare £AFD
924 The politics of the Second Empire £AFD
Missenden Abbey, *Great Missenden*
ARCA

13–15 December
925 Wine appreciation £AFD
926 Watercolour workshop £AFD
927 Alexander Technique £AFD
928 Introduction to Super Highway £AFD
The Old Rectory, *Fittleworth*
ARCA

13–15 December
929 Bridge congress £80–£101*
Snowdonia National Park Centre, *Maentwrog*
ARCA
****Excluding prizes.***

13–15 December
930 Practical opera weekend – *Carmen* £AFD
Univ Cambridge, *Madingley Hall*

13–15 December
931 The archaeology of the Byzantine city £42*
Univ Oxford, *Oxford*
**Tuition fee. Accommodation and meals available.*

13–15 December
932 Christmas music: Debussy and Beethoven £81
933 Advanced Italian £90
Wansfell College, *Theydon Bois*
ARCA

13–15 December
934 Cabinet making – part 3. Handmade furniture £AFD
935 Jewellery in silver £AFD
936 Interior setting with figure – pastels and water-based media £AFD
937 Renaissance courts of Northern Italy £AFD
West Dean College, *Chichester*
ARCA

13–16 December
938 Life casting – from the human body £AFD
West Dean College, *Chichester*
ARCA

14–15 December
939 The Benslow Advent house party £70*
Benslow Music Trust, *Hitchin*
ARCA
**Residential.*

14–15 December
940 The Medieval mystery and miracle plays £55*
Univ Manchester, *Manchester*
**Resident.*

14–15 December
941 Fairy tale Christmas weekend £40
Wedgwood Memorial College, *Barlaston*
ARCA

15–18 December
942 Woodcarving £AFD
West Dean College, *Chichester*
ARCA

15–20 December
943 Traditional hand finishing – part 2 £AFD
944 Watercolour painting – including working from photographs £AFD
West Dean College, *Chichester*
ARCA

16–18 December
945 A literary Christmas £81
Wansfell College, *Theydon Bois*
ARCA

20–22 December
946 Murder at Maryland – literary and historical murders £77–£105
Maryland College, *Woburn*
ARCA

20–22 December
947 Winter landscapes £AFD
948 Painting birds and animals £AFD
949 Music appreciation £AFD
Pendrell Hall College, *Codsall Wood*
ARCA

20–22 December
950 Winter Solstice walking £65
951 Winter Solstice circle dance £65
Wedgwood Memorial College, *Barlaston*
ARCA

23–28 December
952 A country Christmas £210
Beaconhill, *Deal, Kent*

24–27 December
953 Christmas reunion £AFD
Braziers, ***Ipsden***
ARCA

28 December–1 January
954 A Kentish New Year £160
Beaconhill, ***Deal, Kent***

29 December–1 January
955 English folk dance and song £131
Alston Hall Residential College, ***Preston***
ARCA

29 December–1 January
956 Midwinter summer school: music; circle dancing; history of art £135
Braziers, ***Ipsden***
ARCA

29 December–1 January
957 Hogmanay at Higham – Scottish country dancing £AFD
Higham Hall, ***Cockermouth***
ARCA

30 December–1 January
958 New Year course and party £120*
Benslow Music Trust, ***Hitchin***
ARCA
Residential.

■ ■ ■ ■

January 1997

□ □ □ □

1–31 January
959 Basket making with cane £35*
960 Sugarcraft £35*
961 Eggcraft £35*
962 Flower arranging £35*
963 Bonsai £35*
964 Fabric sculpture £35*
965 Decorative interiors and paintwork £35*
966 Stencilling £35*
967 Needlecraft £35*
968 Strawcraft £35*
969 Machine knitting £35*
970 Patchwork and quilting £35*
971 Découpage – 3D £35*
972 Découpage – traditional £35*
973 Drawing, watercolours and oils £35*
974 Gardening skills £35*
975 Rush seating £35*
976 Cane seating £35*
977 Pottery – any Thursday £35*
978 Music – any instrument 2 hours £35*
979 Languages – one hour £15*
980 Birdwatching £40*
981 Furniture restoration – any 2 consecutive days £100
982 Woodwork – any 3 consecutive days £150
Acorn Activities, ***Herefordshire, Shropshire and Wales***
****Per day. Bookings can be made for any number of days.***

2–5 January
983 Bridge: partnership development £121
Wansfell College, ***Theydon Bois***
ARCA

3–5 January
984 Dyeing for patchwork, quilting and embroidery £80
Alston Hall Residential College, ***Preston***
ARCA

3–5 January
985 String chamber music £99*
Benslow Music Trust, *Hitchin*
ARCA
**Residential.*

3–5 January
986 Friendship – the good life £95
987 The discovery of Ancient Egypt £97
Burton Manor College, *South Wirral*
ARCA

3–5 January
988 The Greeks in the West £110
989 Tai Ji £110
Higham Hall, *Cockermouth*
ARCA

3–5 January
990 Murder mystery weekend £97
Knuston Hall, *Irchester*
ARCA

3–5 January
991 Anyone can read music – part 2 £AFD
992 Mid winter painting workshop £AFD
993 UFOs (Embroidery surgery) £AFD
994 Writing biography £AFD
995 The acoustic guitar accompaniment £AFD
Missenden Abbey, *Great Missenden*
ARCA

3–5 January
996 Franz Liszt – man of the century £AFD
997 The Wars of the Roses £AFD
998 The Gothic world £AFD
Univ Cambridge, *Madingley Hall*

3–5 January
999 Pre retirement weekend £AFD
Urchfont Manor College, *Devizes*
ARCA

3–5 January
1000 Birds of the Lea Valley £81
Wansfell College, *Theydon Bois*
ARCA

3–5 January
1001 Painting £AFD
1002 Music £AFD
Wedgwood Memorial College, *Barlaston*
ARCA

3–5 January
1003 Bead making and braiding – inspired by Africa £AFD
1004 Basic blacksmithing £AFD
1005 Exploit your auto camera £AFD
1006 The painted garden £AFD
West Dean College, *Chichester*
ARCA

3–7 January
1007 Snowdonia's hidden haunts £132–£168
Snowdonia National Park Centre, *Maentwrog*
ARCA

3–7 January
1008 Silversmithing and jewellery – advanced £AFD
West Dean College, *Chichester*
ARCA

3–8 January
1009 Rustic furniture for garden and porch £AFD
West Dean College, *Chichester*
ARCA

5–8 January
1010 Watercolour for beginners £AFD
1011 Photographing your work – for artists and craftspeople £AFD
West Dean College, *Chichester*
ARCA

5–10 January
1012 Basic general painting – any medium £AFD
West Dean College, *Chichester*
ARCA

6–8 January
1013 Europe in the Enlightenment £AFD
Urchfont Manor College, *Devizes*
ARCA

6–9 January
1014 Sketching in pen and colour £145
Burton Manor College, *South Wirral*
ARCA

8–10 January
1015 Tool sharpening and preparation for woodworkers and instrument makers £AFD
West Dean College, *Chichester*
ARCA

9–12 January
1016 Sign communication skills stage I module II £AFD
Lancashire College, *Chorley*
ARCA

10–12 January
1017 Massage £89
Braziers, *Ipsden*
ARCA

10–12 January
1018 Belly dancing £95
1019 Beginners' bridge £96
Burton Manor College, *South Wirral*
ARCA

10–12 January
1020 Folk dancing £110*
Dartington Hall, *Totnes, Devon*
**Residential.*

10–12 January
1021 Chinese brushwork £AFD
Dillington House, *Ilminster*
ARCA

10–12 January
1022 Try duplicate bridge £127
Hawthorn Bridge, *Dunstable, Beds*

10–12 January
1023 Singing for the tone deaf £110
1024 Intro to oil painting £110
Higham Hall, *Cockermouth*
ARCA

10–12 January
1025 Floral art £84
1026 Recorder playing £84
1027 Gaelic £84
1028 Architecture of ancient Mediterranean £84
The Hill Residential College, *Abergavenny*
ARCA

10–12 January
1029 Woodcarving £82
1030 Machine knitting £82
1031 Introduction to dressmaking £82
1032 Flowers in Chinese brush painting £82
Horncastle College, *Horncastle*
ARCA

10–12 January
1033 Chopin without tears £87
1034 Performance skills £87
1035 Fabric covered box making £87
1036 Recorders £87
Knuston Hall, *Irchester*
ARCA

10–12 January
1037 Tai Chi Chuan £86
1038 First aid Red Cross module I £86
1039 Introduction to counselling skills £86
1040 Poetry £86
Lancashire College, *Chorley*
ARCA

10–12 January
1041 Bridge £81–£110
Maryland College, *Woburn*
ARCA

ARCA

ARCA
Your Sign of Quality
1
2
8
3
4
5
6
7
9
10
12
11
24
17
13
15
14
16
22
23
19
20
18
25
21
Adult Residential Colleges Association

THE ARCA COLLEGES

Higham Hall; BASSENTHWAITE LAKE, Cockermouth, Cumbria, CA13 9SH Tel: 01768 776 276 Fax: 01768 676 013 1

Alston Hall College; LONGRIDGE, Preston, Lancs PR3 3BP Tel: 01772 784 661 Fax: 01772 785 835 2

Burton Manor College; BURTON, South Wirral, Cheshire L64 5SJ Tel: 0151 336 5172/3 Fax: 0151 336 6586 3

Plas Tan y Bwlch; Snowdonia National Park Study Centre, MAENTWROG, Blaenau Ffestiniog, Gwynedd LL41 3YU Tel: 01766 590 324 Fax: 01766 590 274 4

Wedgwood Memorial College; BARLESTON, Stoke-on-Trent, Staffs ST12 9DG Tel: 01782 372 105 Fax: 01782 372 393 5

Horncastle College; Mareham Road, HORNCASTLE, Lincs LN9 6BW Tel: 01507 522 449 Fax: 01507 524 382 6

Pendrell Hall; CODSALL WOOD, Wolverhampton, Staffs WV8 1QP Tel: 01902 434 112 Fax: 01902 434 117 7

Lancashire College; Southport Road, CHORLEY, Lancashire PR7 1NB Tel: 01257 276 719 Fax: 01257 241 370 8

Knuston Hall; IRCHESTER, Wellingborough, Northants NN9 7EU Tel: 01933 312 104 Fax: 01933 57 596 9

Wensum Lodge; King Street, NORWICH, Norfolk NR1 1QW Tel: 01603 666 021 Fax: 01603 765 633 10

Maryland College; Leighton Street, WOBURN, Beds MK17 9JD Tel: 01525 292 901 Fax: 01525 290 058 11

Watercolour Weeks at Weobley; The Old Corner House, Broad Street, WEOBLEY, Herefordshire HR4 7SA Tel/Fax: 01544 318 548 12

Benslow Music Trust; Little Benslow Hills, HITCHIN, Herts SG4 9RB Tel: 01462 459 446 Fax: 01462 440 171 13

Wansfell College; 30 Piercing Hill, THEYDON BOIS, Epping, Essex CM16 7LF Tel: 01992 813 027 Fax: 01992 814 761 14

Braziers; IPSDEN, Wallingford, Oxon OX10 6AN Tel: 01491 680 221 15

Denman College; MARCHAM, Abingdon, Oxon OX13 6NW Tel: 01865 391 991 Fax: 01865 391 966 16

Missenden Abbey; GREAT MISSENDEN, Bucks HP16 0BD Tel: 01494 890 295/6 Fax: 01494 863 697 17

The Old Rectory; Fittleworth, PULBOROUGH, West Sussex RH20 1HU Tel/Fax: 01798 865 306 18

Urchfont Manor; URCHFONT, Nr Devizes, Wilts SN10 4RG Tel: 01380 840 495 Fax: 01380 840 005 19

Dillington House; ILMINSTER, Somerset TA19 9DT Tel: 01460 52427 Fax: 01460 52433 20

West Dean College; WEST DEAN, Chichester, Sussex PO18 0QZ Tel: 01243 811 301 Fax: 01243 811 343 21

Debden House; Debdon Green, LOUGHTON, Essex IP10 2PA Tel: 0181 508 3008 Fax: 0181 508 0284 22

Hawkwood College; Painswick Old Road, STROUD, Gloucestershire GL6 7QW Tel/Fax: 01453 759 034 23

Belstead House; Belstead, IPSWICH, Suffolk IP8 3NA Tel: 01473 686 321 Fax: 01473 686 664 24

Pyke House; Upper Lake, BATTLE, East Sussex TN33 0AN Tel: 01424 772 495 Fax: 01424 775 041 25

Each college publishes comprehensive information about its courses and activities. Please write, phone or fax for details.

WHAT IS ARCA?

ARCA is a well established association of Residential Colleges for Adult Education, who share a professional approach to education in residential setting.

The ARCA colleges are open to adults of all ages from all walks of life and from all parts of the country and overseas. They specialise in providing residential courses which give study a new dimension, offering freedom from daily routine and the domestic or work environment, in a relaxed, comfortable and secure situation; freedom to discover the pleasure and challenge of study at many different levels, to think and discuss, to enjoy companionship in pleasant surroundings.

The colleges are housed in almost as wide a variety of buildings as the range of courses offered – some are restored and converted country houses, others are adapted Victorian or Edwardian family homes, while some offer purpose-built accommodation. They are pleasantly situated, many with their own grounds and gardens. Each college, in its own individual way has created an atmosphere which makes people feel at home.

Whether a beginner wishing to make a start, or an enthusiast seeking mental refreshment or opportunities for more advanced studies, they will probably find the right course at one or more of the ARCA colleges. Lecturers and tutors are usually resident too, so there is plenty of scope for informal questions and discussion over a meal or a drink at the bar.

Courses offered at the ARCA colleges cover the broadest possible spectrum of subjects, some leading to qualifications while others involve studying for the pleasure alone. Literature, Creative Writing, Music – both practical and appreciation, History, Archaeology, Local History, Natural History, Art History, Painting, Crafts of all kinds, Calligraphy, Travel, Geography, Environmental topics, Needlecrafts, 'Access' courses, Personal Development... the list goes on and on... learning at its best with stimulus, freedom and flexibility of method.

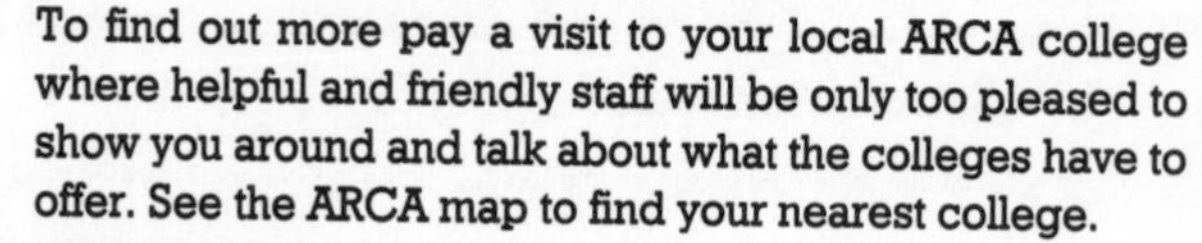
To find out more pay a visit to your local ARCA college where helpful and friendly staff will be only too pleased to show you around and talk about what the colleges have to offer. See the ARCA map to find your nearest college.

Is Your Sign of Quality

10–12 January
1042 Verdi: opera for all £AFD
1043 Colour and colour mixing in watercolour £AFD
1044 Winter landscape painting £AFD
1045 C&G basketry – plaited baskets £AFD
1046 Bridal millinery £AFD
1047 The Silk Route £AFD
1048 Spanish intermediate £AFD
At the Misbourne School
1049 Painting, an introduction to painting techniques £AFD
1050 An introduction to dyeing £AFD
1051 Effects with marbling £AFD
1052 3-D Découpage £AFD
1053 Oriental paper crafts £AFD
1054 Designs on leather £AFD
1055 Jewellery £AFD
1056 Prevent food poisoning £AFD
1057 Producing an oral history of Missenden Abbey £AFD
Missenden Abbey, *Great Missenden*
ARCA

10–12 January
1058 Cwrs Blynyddol Cymraeg £68–£86
1059 Gwneud Dillad/Sampleri Cymraeg £68–£86
Snowdonia National Park Centre, *Maentwrog*
ARCA

10–12 January
1060 History of English furniture 1500–1830 £AFD
1061 The folklore of the Fens £AFD
1062 Italian weekend £AFD
1063 The thousand and one knights £AFD
Univ Cambridge, *Madingley Hall*

10–12 January
1064 The later 18th-century great house £47*
Univ Oxford, *Oxford*
****Tuition fee. Accommodation and meals available.***

10–12 January
1065 ***Othello* – from play to opera** £AFD
1066 Hand colour black and white photographs £AFD
Urchfont Manor College, *Devizes*
ARCA

10–12 January
1067 French for the rusty £81
1068 A positive approach to management £81
1069 Films of David Lean £81
1070 Freelance journalism £81
Wansfell College, *Theydon Bois*
ARCA

10–12 January
1071 Pottery – throwing and turning £AFD
1072 Glass engraving for beginners £AFD
1073 Cartoon drawing £AFD
1074 Creative control of your SLR camera £AFD
West Dean College, *Chichester*
ARCA

11–12 January
1075 Creative thinking, planning and solving difficulties £45
Braziers, *Ipsden*
ARCA

11–12 January
1076 Contemporary history £36
1077 Music £36
1078 Philosophy £36
Wedgwood Memorial College, *Barlaston*
ARCA

12–15 January
1079 Developing sketches into final work £AFD
1080 Designing a jumper – from inspiration to knitting pattern £AFD
West Dean College, *Chichester*
ARCA

12–17 January
1081 Cabinet making – part 2 £AFD
1082 General painting – emphasis on colour £AFD
West Dean College, *Chichester*
ARCA

17–19 January
1083 An evening at the opera – *Manon* £80
Alston Hall Residential College, ***Preston***
ARCA

17–19 January
1084 Stillness and stress £AFD
Ammerdown Centre, ***Radstock, Bath***

17–19 January
1085 Certificated first aid course £150
Braziers, ***Ipsden***
ARCA

17–19 January
1086 Alexander Technique £95
Burton Manor College, ***South Wirral***
ARCA

17–19 January
1087 Lace making £AFD
Dartington Hall, ***Totnes, Devon***

17–19 January
1088 Italian £AFD
Dillington House, ***Ilminster***
ARCA

17–19 January
1089 Instructions for the defence £127
Hawthorn Bridge, ***Dunstable, Beds***

17–19 January
1090 Portrait drawing £110
1091 Beginners guide to the camcorder £110
Higham Hall, ***Cockermouth***
ARCA

17–19 January
1092 Alexander Technique £84
1093 Painting with water £84
1094 What's in a word £84
1095 Jane Austen £84
1096 History of the Welsh Marches £84
The Hill Residential College, ***Abergavenny***
ARCA

17–19 January
1097 Creative lace £82
Horncastle College, ***Horncastle***
ARCA

17–19 January
1098 Astronomy – The night sky £87
1099 Lacemaking for all £87
1100 The great metropolis – London £87
1101 Discovering geology £87
Knuston Hall, ***Irchester***
ARCA

17–19 January
1102 Gold thread embroidery £86
1103 Yoga £86
1104 Reflextherapy £86
1105 Family history £86
Lancashire College, ***Chorley***
ARCA

17–19 January
1106 Scottish dancing £71–£99
Maryland College, ***Woburn***
ARCA

17–19 January
1107 Hedd Wyn – Wales' answer to Wilfred Owen? £55
Meirionnydd Languages, ***North Wales***

17–19 January
1108 The erotic in art and music £AFD
1109 Wet into wet watercolour painting £AFD
1110 Passementerie £AFD
1111 C&G embroidery part 1 year 2 £AFD
1112 Preparing working designs £AFD
1113 The folklore of winter: ploughs, bears and mumming £AFD
1114 Graphology £AFD
1115 New dream journeys – a writing course £AFD
Missenden Abbey, ***Great Missenden***
ARCA

MISSENDEN ABBEY

your FIRST CHOICE for WEEKENDS EASTER and SUMMER SCHOOLS

FIRST CLASS ACCOMMODATION – luxury study bedrooms all with private bathroom – dining rooms, library and garden room with ornate plaster work and ash panelling, a licensed bar, sports facilities and a peaceful listed garden.

FIRST CLASS TUITION – Nationally acclaimed tutors provide courses in the arts, crafts and humanities: they offer exciting themes, new insights and discoveries: the groundwork and inspiration to carry on where the course leaves off. Beginners and specialists alike find themselves working to the highest standards and enjoying every minute!

Make **MISSENDEN ABBEY** in Buckinghamshire your **FIRST CHOICE** for weekend breaks and your **FIRST CHOICE** for Summer School.

Easily accessible – M1 – M25 (15 mins).
British Rail – Marylebone (40 mins).

Programmes for Weekends and Summer School from
Missenden Abbey, Gt. Missenden
Bucks HP16 0BD Tel: 01494 890295/6

Adult Continuing Education Service
Buckingham County Council

17–19 January
1116 Atmospheric watercolours £AFD
1117 Singing for the tone deaf £AFD
1118 How to be a freelance journalist £AFD
The Old Rectory, *Fittleworth*
ARCA

17–19 January
1119 Writers Austen Read £AFD
1120 Bertrand Russell £AFD
1121 What mean these stones? £AFD
1122 Reading Latin £AFD
Univ Cambridge, *Madingley Hall*

17–19 January
1123 Archaeology: Carthage versus Rome £AFD
Urchfont Manor College, *Devizes*
ARCA

17–19 January
1124 Copper and pewterwork £81
1125 Gilbert and Sullivan £81
1126 Colour studies £81
Wansfell College, *Theydon Bois*
ARCA

17–19 January
1127 Understanding watercolour £AFD
Watercolour Weeks at Weobley, *Herefordshire*
ARCA

18–19 January
1128 Alan Bennett £AFD
Univ Manchester, *Manchester*

18–19 January
1129 Using title deeds for local history £45*
Univ Oxford, *Oxford*
****Tuition fee. Accommodation and meals available.***

18–19 January
1130 Women in literature £36
Wedgwood Memorial College, *Barlaston*
ARCA

19–22 January
1131 Silk painting for beginners £AFD
1132 Mounting and framing pictures £AFD
1133 Drawing and painting with artificial light £AFD
West Dean College, *Chichester*
ARCA

19–24 January
1134 Silversmithing £AFD
1135 Strength and adventure in watercolour £AFD
West Dean College, *Chichester*
ARCA

20–23 January
1136 Floristry £118
Alston Hall Residential College, *Preston*
ARCA

20–24 January
1137 Canvas work – traditional and modern £AFD
1138 Dolls house workshop £AFD
1139 Card and board games £AFD
The Old Rectory, *Fittleworth*
ARCA

20–25 January
1140 Beginners Welsh £125
Meirionnydd Languages, *North Wales*

22–24 January
1141 Miniature woodturning for beginners £AFD
West Dean College, *Chichester*
ARCA

24–26 January
1142 Circle dance £AFD
1143 Mantras in movement £AFD
Ammerdown Centre, *Radstock, Bath*

24–26 January
1144 Italian madrigals £115*
1145 Alexander Technique £110*
Benslow Music Trust, *Hitchin*
ARCA
****Residential.***

24–26 January
1146 Law in crisis £89
Braziers, *Ipsden*
ARCA

24–26 January
1147 Wine and Spirit Education Trust Certificate £95
Burton Manor College, *South Wirral*
ARCA

24–26 January
1148 Picture framing £AFD
1149 Camcorders (experienced) £AFD
1150 Three stages of opera – II £AFD
Dillington House, *Ilminster*
ARCA

24–26 January
1151 Beginners guide to the symphony £110
1152 Confidence building for women £110
1153 Drawing with crayons £110
Higham Hall, *Cockermouth*
ARCA

24–26 January
1154 Fundamentals of picture making £84
1155 Bridge £84
The Hill Residential College, *Abergavenny*
ARCA

24–26 January
1156 Woodturning £82
1157 Glasscraft £82
Horncastle College, *Horncastle*
ARCA

24–26 January
1158 Ancient Greece £95
Knuston Hall, *Irchester*
ARCA

24–26 January
1159 Alexander Technique £86
1160 Accelerate your learning £86
1161 Picture framing £86
1162 Sound recording £86
Lancashire College, *Chorley*
ARCA

24–26 January
1163 Lacemaking £71–£99
Maryland College, *Woburn*
ARCA

24–26 January
1164 Machine knitting – design to finished jacket £AFD
1165 Miniaturists of the north £AFD
1166 Mendelssohn's Scottish journey £AFD
1167 Bridge for the absolute beginner £AFD
1168 The best of human nature £AFD
1169 Visual arts – 1880–1910 £AFD
1170 Nessie – reality from the murky deep £AFD
1171 The view from the trenches – soldiers in the First World War £AFD
Missenden Abbey, *Great Missenden*
ARCA

24–26 January
1172 Stockmarket and investment for beginners £AFD
1173 Computers without consternation £AFD
1174 Pewter workshop £AFD
1175 Drawing for the terrified £AFD
The Old Rectory, *Fittleworth*
ARCA

24–26 January
1176 Cold porcelain £AFD
1177 Improvers' bridge £AFD
1178 Personal development £AFD
Pendrell Hall College, *Codsall Wood*
ARCA

24–26 January
1179 Adar y Gaeaf £68–£86
Snowdonia National Park Centre, *Maentwrog*
ARCA

24–26 January
1180 Early modern women lives £AFD
1181 Reading classical Greek £AFD
1182 The Great War in literature £AFD
Univ Cambridge, *Madingley Hall*

24–26 January
1183 Writing poetry £42*
Univ Oxford, *Oxford*
Tuition fee. Accommodation and meals available.

24–26 January
1184 Beginners water colour £AFD
1185 Folklore of Wiltshire £AFD
Urchfont Manor College, *Devizes*
ARCA

24–26 January
1186 Introduction to counselling £81
1187 Wagner's ***Parsifal*** £81
1188 Photography: advanced monochrome printing £98
1189 Embroidery: felt inspired £81
Wansfell College, *Theydon Bois*
ARCA

25–27 January
1190 Esperanto festival £65
Wedgwood Memorial College, *Barlaston*
ARCA

26–29 January
1191 Caring for and refinishing antique furniture £AFD
1192 Beginners – watercolour £AFD
West Dean College, *Chichester*
ARCA

26–31 January
1193 Style, taste and interpretation in piano music £AFD
Higham Hall, *Cockermouth*
ARCA

26–31 January
1194 Gilding – part 2 £AFD
1195 Strength and adventure in watercolour £AFD
West Dean College, *Chichester*
ARCA

27–29 January
1196 Government in action £91
Wansfell College, *Theydon Bois*
ARCA

27–30 January
1197 The saxophone experience £142*
Benslow Music Trust, *Hitchin*
ARCA
Residential.

27–30 January
1198 Dyed and machine embroidered pictures £49
The Gateway, *Shrewsbury*
Local accommodation is arranged separately on request.

31 January–2 February
1199 Drawing for the terrified, part one £80
1200 Life drawing – a further study £85
Alston Hall Residential College, *Preston*
ARCA

31 January–2 February
1201 Spirit in movement, mind in matter £AFD
Ammerdown Centre, *Radstock, Bath*

31 January–2 February
1202 Folk dance musicians £95
Belstead House, *Ipswich*
ARCA

31 January–2 February
1203 String orchestra £110*
1204 String and piano ensembles £140*
Benslow Music Trust, *Hitchin*
ARCA
Residential.

31 January–2 February

1205 Another way of being £89
1206 The story of Nottingham lace £89

Braziers, *Ipsden*
ARCA

31 January–2 February

1207 Develop your writing power £95
1208 Wildlife in watercolour £95

Burton Manor College, *South Wirral*
ARCA

31 January–2 February

1209 Writing your life story £AFD

Dillington House, *Ilminster*
ARCA

31 January–2 February

1210 Spanish wines £AFD
1211 Jazz appreciation £110

Higham Hall, *Cockermouth*
ARCA

31 January–2 February

1212 Unlocking your voice £84
1213 In the beginning . . . Wales £84

The Hill Residential College, *Abergavenny*
ARCA

31 January–2 February

1214 Bridge for improvers £87
1215 Laugh and be well £87
1216 Wood carving £87
1217 A jigsaw puzzle £87

Knuston Hall, *Irchester*
ARCA

31 January–2 February

1218 Spanish all levels £86

Lancashire College, *Chorley*
ARCA

31 January–2 February

1219 Visconti and the German dream £71–£99
1220 Oscar Wilde and his circle £71–£99

Maryland College, *Woburn*
ARCA

31 January–2 February

1221 Towards the Millenium 1920–1930 £AFD
1222 Art studio: ref Renoir and Lautrec £AFD
1223 C&G interior design £AFD
1224 Machine embroidery £AFD
1225 C&G patchwork and quilting £AFD
1226 Contemporary British poetry £AFD
1227 Spanish literature: ***La Casa de Bernarda Alba*** £AFD
1228 Promote yourself £AFD

Missenden Abbey, *Great Missenden*
ARCA

31 January–2 February

1229 Painting interiors £AFD
1230 The miracle of the symphony orchestra £AFD
1231 English architecture at a glance £AFD

The Old Rectory, *Fittleworth*
ARCA

31 January–2 February

1232 The Duke of Wellington as a great commander £AFD
1233 Milton and Marvell: poetry, prose and politics £AFD
1234 The history of Britain's birds and birdwaters £AFD
1235 Exploring the mind £AFD

Univ Cambridge, *Madingley Hall*

31 January–2 February

1236 Culture and belief in Europe 1450–1600 £AFD

Urchfont Manor College, *Devizes*
ARCA

31 January–2 February

1237 Exploring the Eastern Orthodox world £81
1238 Life and leisure of the elite 1714–1789 £81
1239 The poetry of Wordsworth £81

Wansfell College, *Theydon Bois*
ARCA

31 January–2 February
1240 Understanding watercolour £AFD
Watercolour Weeks at Weobley, *Herefordshire*
ARCA

31 January–2 February
1241 Woodturning between centres or spindle turning including green wood £AFD
1242 Traditional upholstery for beginners £AFD
1243 Still life – towards abstraction £AFD
1244 An introduction to Persian carpets – history, design, colour, care and repair £AFD
1245 Intensive drawing £AFD
1246 The three ages of opera – Montiverdi to Mozart £AFD
West Dean College, *Chichester*
ARCA

31 January–3 February
1247 Enamelling on silver – advanced £AFD
West Dean College, *Chichester*
ARCA

■ ■ ■ ■

February 1997

□ □ □ □

1–2 February
1248 Portrait drawing £22
1249 Make a traditional teddy bear £24
The Gateway, *Shrewsbury*
Local accommodation is arranged separately on request.

1–2 February
1250 The Spanish Civil War £29*
Univ Oxford, *Oxford*
****Tuition fee. Accommodation and meals available.***

1–2 February
1251 Spanish £50
Wedgwood Memorial College, *Barlaston*
ARCA

1–28 February
1252 Basket making with cane £35*
1253 Sugarcraft £35*
1254 Eggcraft £35*
1255 Flower arranging £35*
1256 Bonsai £35*
1257 Fabric sculpture £35*
1258 Decorative interiors and paintwork £35*
1259 Stencilling £35*
1260 Needlecraft £35*
1261 Strawcraft £35*
1262 Machine knitting £35*
1263 Patchwork and quilting £35*
1264 Découpage – 3D £35*
1265 Découpage – traditional £35*
1266 Drawing, watercolours and oils £35*
1267 Gardening skills £35*
1268 Rush seating £35*
1269 Cane seating £35*
1270 Pottery – any Thursday £35*
1271 Music – any instrument 2 hours £35*
1272 Languages – one hour £15*
1273 Birdwatching £40*
1274 Furniture restoration – any 2 consecutive days £100
1275 Woodwork – any 3 consecutive days £150
Acorn Activities, *Herefordshire, Shropshire and Wales*
****Per day. Bookings can be made for any number of days.***

2–5 February
1276 Traditional canvas work £AFD
West Dean College, *Chichester*
ARCA

2–6 February
1277 Bookbinding – case bindings for magazines and journals £AFD
West Dean College, *Chichester*
ARCA

2–7 February
1278 Shipwrights' workshop – boat repair – traditional techniques £AFD
1279 Life modelling in terracotta £AFD
West Dean College, *Chichester*
ARCA

2–8 February
1280 Beginners Russian £125
Meirionnydd Languages, *North Wales*

3–6 February
1281 Viol consorts £132*
Benslow Music Trust, *Hitchin*
ARCA
****Residential.***

3–7 February
1282 Beginners bridge £AFD
1283 Drawing and painting from photographs £AFD
1284 Exploring your family history £AFD
The Old Rectory, *Fittleworth*
ARCA

6–9 February
1285 Aconites and snowdrops £105
Beaconhill, *Deal, Kent*

7–9 February
1286 Appliqué for quilters £80
Alston Hall Residential College, *Preston*
ARCA

7–9 February
1287 Brass ensembles £115*
1288 Choral weekend £105*
Benslow Music Trust, *Hitchin*
ARCA
****Residential.***

7–9 February
1289 Teilhard de Chardin course £89
Braziers, *Ipsden*
ARCA

7–9 February
1290 Introduction to aromatherapy £95
1291 Family and community history £92
1292 Print workshop £99
Burton Manor College, *South Wirral*
ARCA

7–9 February
1293 Mah Jong £AFD
1294 Heirloom doll making £AFD
Dillington House, *Ilminster*
ARCA

7–9 February
1295 Bridge: practise your card play £135
Hawthorn Bridge, *Romsey, Hants*

7–9 February
1296 Singing for the tone deaf £110
1297 Flower painting £110
Higham Hall, *Cockermouth*
ARCA

7–9 February
1298 Safeguarding the past £84
1299 Introduction of philosophy £84
1300 Welsh £84
The Hill Residential College, *Abergavenny*
ARCA

7–9 February
1301 Identification of lace £87
1302 Italian literature £87
1303 French intermediate £87
1304 Aspects of pastel £87
Knuston Hall, *Irchester*
ARCA

7–9 February
1305 French all levels £86
Lancashire College, *Chorley*
ARCA

7–9 February
1306 Oil painting – the still life £71–£99
1307 The story of the English house £71–£99
Maryland College, *Woburn*
ARCA

7–9 February
1308 Portrait drawing and painting £AFD
1309 C&G embroidery part 2 year 2 £AFD
1310 C&G embroidery part 2 year 1 £AFD
1311 Exploring crazy patchwork £AFD
1312 Tai Ji Quan £AFD
1313 Getting to grips with numbers £AFD
1314 The uses and abuses of the Victorian censuses £AFD
At the Misbourne School
1315 Painting, working with opaque paints £AFD
1316 Drawing for the terrified I £AFD
1317 Chinese painting £AFD
1318 Textiles in the round £AFD
1319 Fabric fun with microwave dyes £AFD
1320 Woodcarving C&G and beyond £AFD
1321 Stained glass £AFD
1322 Lettering and handtooling for bound books £AFD
Missenden Abbey, *Great Missenden*
ARCA

7–9 February
1323 Lloyd George £AFD
1324 Getting started in watercolour £AFD
1325 Making dolls house dolls £AFD
1326 Introduction to flying £AFD
The Old Rectory, *Fittleworth*
ARCA

7–9 February
1327 Llen Gwerin ein Bywyd Cyhoeddus £68–£86
Snowdonia National Park Centre, *Maentwrog*
ARCA

7–9 February
1328 Monteverdi's Vespers £AFD
1329 Art and architecture HANSA Teutonic order £AFD
1330 Advanced geneology. Family history £AFD
Univ Cambridge, *Madingley Hall*

7–9 February
1331 Iron Age Britain £42*
Univ Oxford, *Oxford*
****Tuition fee. Accommodation and meals available.***

7–9 February
1332 Padded, layered and raised embroidery £AFD
1333 Singing for fun £AFD
Urchfont Manor College, *Devizes*
ARCA

7–9 February
1334 Archaeology of Egypt: 1550–1470 BC £81
1335 Alexander Technique £81
1336 German language through literature – improvers £86
Wansfell College, *Theydon Bois*
ARCA

7–9 February
1337 Cabinet making – part 1 £AFD
1338 Decorative paint techniques £AFD
1339 Traditional woodcarving for beginners £AFD
1340 Drawing for painting £AFD
1341 Honiton lace and needle lace £AFD
1342 Blacksmithing – cage, rope twist and other decorative handles £AFD
West Dean College, *Chichester*
ARCA

LITTLE BENSLOW HILLS

Residential Centre for Music Courses

owned and run by

Benslow Music Trust

an independent educational charity.

Set in peaceful wooded grounds in Hichin, Herts, 'Benslow' is a unique centre for the study and practice of music. Our programme offers some 100 courses a year including chamber music, jazz, big band, recorders, orchestras, early music, Baroque Opera, brass ensembles, saxophone, harp, keyboards and piano, Alexander Technique and choral singing.

Choose from weekend and holiday courses throughout the year with experienced, friendly tuition amongst like-minded people in a specialist centre. We are 30 minutes from Kings Cross and 10 minutes from the A1(M).

Send for our programme:-
Benslow Music Trust
Little Benslow Hills
Hitchin, Herts SG4 9RB
Tel: 01462 459446
Fax: 01462 440171

8–9 February
1343 Tutorial – Contemporary history £36
1344 Tutorial – music £36
1345 Tutorial – philosophy £36
Wedgwood Memorial College, *Barlaston*
ARCA

9–11 February
1346 How to write short stories £76
Lancashire College, *Chorley*
ARCA

9–12 February
1347 Mounting and framing pictures £AFD
1348 Hand spinning and yarn design with wool and silk £AFD
1349 Write a successful novel £AFD
West Dean College, *Chichester*
ARCA

9–13 February
1350 Bridge £AFD
Higham Hall, *Cockermouth*
ARCA

9–13 February
1351 Tucks, textures and pleats in plain fabric £AFD
1352 Painting on silk and velvet £AFD
West Dean College, *Chichester*
ARCA

9–14 February
1353 A week of hopeless adventure! £165–£210
Snowdonia National Park Centre, *Maentwrog*
ARCA

9–14 February
1354 Glass engraving in stipple and line £AFD
1355 Dream, imagination and surrealism in painting £AFD
West Dean College, *Chichester*
ARCA

10–12 February
1356 Practical painting £81
1357 Britain and the East in the C17th £81
Wansfell College, *Theydon Bois*
ARCA

10–13 February
1358 String chamber music £129*
Benslow Music Trust, *Hitchin*
ARCA
**Residential.*

10–13 February
1359 Embroidery £AFD
Dartington Hall, *Totnes, Devon*

10–14 February
1360 Painting course £128
Wedgwood Memorial College, *Barlaston*
ARCA

11–13 February
1361 Calligraphy £76
Lancashire College, *Chorley*
ARCA

12–14 February
1362 Pudding Lane to Pie Corner £91
1363 Exploring cross stitch £81
Wansfell College, *Theydon Bois*
ARCA

13–16 February
1364 Country weekend with music £105
Beaconhill, *Deal, Kent*

13–16 February
1365 Practical wood machining £AFD
West Dean College, *Chichester*
ARCA

14–16 February
1366 Intermediate wind chamber music £111*
Benslow Music Trust, *Hitchin*
ARCA
**Residential.*

4–16 February
1367 Tai Chi £89
1368 Calligraphy £89
Braziers, *Ipsden*
ARCA

14–16 February
1369 Residential bridge £96
1370 Apre Film Noir £97
Burton Manor College, *South Wirral*
ARCA

14–16 February
1371 New science £AFD
Dartington Hall, *Totnes, Devon*

14–16 February
1372 Introducing/revising uncials £AFD
Dillington House, *Ilminster*
ARCA

14–16 February
1373 Cartoon drawing £110
1374 Intro to aromatherapy £110
Higham Hall, *Cockermouth*
ARCA

14–16 February
1375 Karate £84
1376 Making the most of your voice £84
1377 Snowscenes £84
The Hill Residential College, *Abergavenny*
ARCA

14–16 February
1378 Move and stretch £87
1379 Parchment craft £87
1380 Ancient Greece for the modern traveller £87
1381 Seven journeys to the Celtic legendworld £87
Knuston Hall, *Irchester*
ARCA

14–16 February
1382 Mahler £71–£99
1383 Intermediate French conversation £71–£99
Maryland College, *Woburn*
ARCA

14–16 February
1384 Saints Saens, Saties and Les Six £AFD
1385 Still life: Chardin and Morandi £AFD
1386 Traditional and contemporary quilting £AFD
1387 Bedfordshire lace at all stages £AFD
1388 Silk ribbon embroidery – BOCN £AFD
1389 Oriental porcelain for the West £AFD
1390 Learning German through literature – intermediate/advanced £AFD
1391 French conversation – advanced £AFD
1392 A feast of valentines £AFD
Missenden Abbey, *Great Missenden*
ARCA

14–16 February
1393 Church wall paintings £AFD
1394 Woodcarving £AFD
1395 Lace making £AFD
1396 Chinese brush painting £AFD
The Old Rectory, *Fittleworth*
ARCA

14–16 February
1397 And so to bed: the world of Samuel Pepys £AFD
1398 From cylinders to CDs: the story of recorded sound £AFD
1399 Life and death in ancient Egypt £AFD
Univ Cambridge, *Madingley Hall*

14–16 February
1400 Brahms' and Mendelsohn – a double anniversary £AFD
1401 Willow basket making £AFD
1402 Love poetry – a many splendoured thing £AFD
Urchfont Manor College, *Devizes*
ARCA

14–16 February
1403 Workshop for singers £87
1404 German conversation £81
1405 Wilkie Collins and the classic English murder mystery £81
Wansfell College, *Theydon Bois*
ARCA

14–16 February
1406 Understanding watercolour £AFD
Watercolour Weeks at Weobley, *Herefordshire*
ARCA

14–16 February
1407 Bowl turning £AFD
1408 Silversmithing – polishing £AFD
1409 Oil painting £AFD
1410 Beaded bags and tassels £AFD
1411 Renaissance music weekend £AFD
1412 Reducing the garden workload £AFD
West Dean College, *Chichester*
ARCA

15–16 February
1413 Painting weekend £20
1414 Writing your life story £19
The Gateway, *Shrewsbury*
Local accommodation is arranged separately on request.

15–16 February
1415 Choral weekend £AFD
1416 Music appreciation £AFD
Univ Manchester, *Manchester*

15–16 February
1417 Tutorial – women in literature £36
Wedgwood Memorial College, *Barlaston*
ARCA

16–19 February
1418 General silversmithing £AFD
1419 Window drapery – blind making £AFD
West Dean College, *Chichester*
ARCA

16–21 February
1420 Woodturning £AFD
1421 Pottery general £AFD
1422 Life drawing and painting – towards abstraction £AFD
West Dean College, *Chichester*
ARCA

17–19 February
1423 Practical lace £89
Horncastle College, *Horncastle*
ARCA

17–20 February
1424 Let's play jazz! £135*
1425 Elementary recorder ensemble £135*
Benslow Music Trust, *Hitchin*
ARCA
****Residential.***

17–20 February
1426 Woodcarving £42
The Gateway, *Shrewsbury*
Local accommodation is arranged separately on request.

17–21 February
1427 Early spring study week £185*
Ford Castle, *Berwick-upon-Tweed*
****Single room.***

17–21 February
1428 Improve your bridge: intermediate £235/£245
Hawthorn Bridge, *Alfriston, Sussex*

17–21 February
1429 Play reading £AFD
1430 Clock repair £AFD
1431 Starting out in singing £AFD
The Old Rectory, *Fittleworth*
ARCA

17–21 February
1432 Bookbinding workshop £AFD
Urchfont Manor College, *Devizes*
ARCA

18–20 February
1433 Creative textiles £36
The Gateway, *Shrewsbury*
Local accommodation is arranged separately on request.

19–21 February
1434 Painting miniatures £36
The Gateway, ***Shrewsbury***
Local accommodation is arranged separately on request.

20–21 February
1435 Pompeii and Heraculaneum £26
The Gateway, ***Shrewsbury***
Local accommodation is arranged separately on request.

20–23 February
1436 The countryside in early spring £105
Beaconhill, ***Deal, Kent***

20–23 February
1437 Sign communication skills stage III module II £AFD
Lancashire College, ***Chorley***
ARCA

21–23 February
1438 Recorder playing workshop £80
1439 Tai Ji and Qigong £80
Alston Hall Residential College, ***Preston***
ARCA

21–23 February
1440 Patchwork and quilting £95
Belstead House, ***Ipswich***
ARCA

21–23 February
1441 Elementary strings £104*
1442 Jazz guitar £105*
1443 Compleat recorder £105*
Benslow Music Trust, ***Hitchin***
ARCA
****Residential.***

21–23 February
1444 The ancient wars £89
1445 The Impressionists £89
Braziers, ***Ipsden***
ARCA

21–23 February
1446 Wine and Spirit Education Trust Certificate £95
Burton Manor College, ***South Wirral***
ARCA

21–23 February
1447 Mind of music £AFD
1448 Italian language and culture £AFD
Dartington Hall, ***Totnes, Devon***

21–23 February
1449 Seamen & smugglers £AFD
Dillington House, ***Ilminster***
ARCA

21–23 February
1450 Roman archaeology £110
1451 Picture framing £110
Higham Hall, ***Cockermouth***
ARCA

21–23 February
1452 Freedom in water colour £84
1453 Music appreciation £84
The Hill Residential College, ***Abergavenny***
ARCA

21–23 February
1454 Calligraphy £82
1455 Revel in retirement £82
Horncastle College, ***Horncastle***
ARCA

21–23 February
1456 Learning German through literature £87
1457 Machine embroidery £87
1458 World of floristry £87
1459 Mah Jong addicts weekend £87
Knuston Hall, ***Irchester***
ARCA

21–23 February
1460 Introduction to alternative therapies £86
1461 Introduction to counselling skills £86
1462 Window furnishings £86
1463 Transactional analysis £86
Lancashire College, *Chorley*
ARCA

21–23 February
1464 George Sand £71–£99
1465 Kipling and Lear £71–£99
Maryland College, *Woburn*
ARCA

21–23 February
1466 Russian poetry and songs £55
Meirionnydd Languages, *North Wales*

21–23 February
1467 A guide to Russian opera £AFD
1468 Life drawing £AFD
1469 Crochet with texture £AFD
1470 Comedy writing £AFD
1471 An architectural study – the growth of London 1800–2000 £AFD
1472 Business start-up (for women) £AFD
1473 Contemporary political issues £AFD
Missenden Abbey, *Great Missenden*
ARCA

21–23 February
1474 The beguiling medium (watercolour) £AFD
1475 French £AFD
1476 St John lifesaver course £AFD
1477 Machine embroidery £AFD
The Old Rectory, *Fittleworth*
ARCA

21–23 February
1478 Chinese brush painting £AFD
1479 Recorder playing £AFD
Pendrell Hall College, *Codsall Wood*
ARCA

21–23 February
1480 Weekend for singers, conductors and teachers £90
Sing for Pleasure, *Bourton on the Water, Oxon*

21–23 February
1481 Craft weekend £68–£86
Snowdonka National Park Centre, *Maentwrog*
ARCA

21–23 February
1482 A various universe: Indian art and architecture £AFD
1483 Reading classical Greek advanced £AFD
1484 Richard the Lionheart and the third crusade £AFD
Univ Cambridge, *Madingley Hall*

21–23 February
1485 History of costume £AFD
Urchfont Manor College, *Devizes*
ARCA

21–23 February
1486 Family history workshop £81
1487 Scottish Gaelic £81
Wansfell College, *Theydon Bois*
ARCA

21–23 February
1488 Cane and rush seating £AFD
1489 Portrait miniatures from life £AFD
1490 Colour in calligraphy £AFD
1491 Atmospheric watercolours £AFD
1492 Solo singers wishing to improve their technique £AFD
West Dean College, *Chichester*
ARCA

21–24 February
1493 Mosaics in marble, glass and stone £AFD
West Dean College, *Chichester*
ARCA

21–28 February
1494 Modelling from life with casting in ciment fondu £AFD
West Dean College, *Chichester*
ARCA

22–23 February
1495 Chinese brush painting £20
1496 Rag rug making £21
The Gateway, *Shrewsbury*
Local accommodation is arranged separately on request.

23–27 February
1497 Creative video workshop £AFD
West Dean College, *Chichester*
ARCA

23–28 February
1498 The multimedia roadshow £AFD
Higham Hall, *Cockermouth*
ARCA

23–28 February
1499 Repairing and refinishing antique furniture £AFD
1500 Still life – water based media £AFD
1501 Writing and illustrating books for children £AFD
West Dean College, *Chichester*
ARCA

24–28 February
1502 Painting the winter scene £160
1503 Machine knitting. Ribber works for colour £160
Alston Hall Residential College, *Preston*
ARCA

24–28 February
1504 Design for church embroidery £AFD
Urchfont Manor College, *Devizes*
ARCA

27 February–2 March
1505 Walking weekend £105
Beaconhill, *Deal, Kent*

28 February–2 March
1506 Embroidered fabric covered boxes £160
1507 Drawing for the terrified, part two £80
Alston Hall Residential College, *Preston*
ARCA

28 February–2 March
1508 Creative writing £95
Belstead House, *Ipswich*
ARCA

28 February–2 March
1509 Wind chamber music £110*
Benslow Music Trust, *Hitchin*
ARCA
****Residential.***

28 February–2 March
1510 Language weekend – German, Dutch and Scandinavian languages £59–£130
Brasshouse Centre, *Birmingham*

28 February–2 March
1511 Dreamwork £AFD
Dartington Hall, *Totnes, Devon*

28 February–2 March
1512 Arts in the age of Charles I £AFD
1513 Jane Austen . . . £AFD
Dillington House, *Ilminster*
ARCA

28 February–2 March
1514 The sacred space of the word £90/£98
Hawkwood College, *Stroud*
ARCA

28 February–2 March
1515 Patchwork £110
1516 Spinners workshop £110
Higham Hall, *Cockermouth*
ARCA

28 February–2 March
1517 Crochet £84
1518 Mounting pictures £84
1519 Writers' workshop £84
The Hill Residential College, *Abergavenny*
ARCA

28 February–2 March
1520 Bridge £82
1521 Garden design £82
1522 Picture framing £82
1523 Making clay buildings (build a miniature street!) £82
Horncastle College, *Horncastle*
ARCA

28 February–2 March
1524 Computing with Windows £89
1525 Positive ageing £87
1526 Miniature painting and silhouettes £87
1527 Strings weekend £AFD
Knuston Hall, *Irchester*
ARCA

28 February–2 March
1528 Espana Actual £86
1529 German all levels £86
1530 First aid module II £86
Lancashire College, *Chorley*
ARCA

28 February–2 March
1531 Persia's lost millenium £71–£99
1532 Garden design £71–£99
Maryland College, *Woburn*
ARCA

28 February–2 March
1533 Introduction to Welsh £55
Meirionnydd Languages, *North Wales*

28 February–2 March
1534 Begin to sing £AFD
1535 The Arabesque – ref: Delacroix/Matisse £AFD
1536 Machine knitting – design to finished jacket £AFD
1537 C&G embroidery part 1 year 2 £AFD
1538 How to be a film critic £AFD
1539 French – intermediate £AFD
1540 The United Nations: reform and renewal £AFD
1541 Machiavelli £AFD
Missenden Abbey, *Great Missenden*
ARCA

28 February–2 March
1542 Miniature painting £AFD
1543 Introduction to ceramic restoration £AFD
1544 How poetry works £AFD
The Old Rectory, *Fittleworth*
ARCA

28 February–2 March
1545 Art in the balance £AFD
1546 Paleography of Tudors and Stuarts £AFD
1547 First person Dickens £AFD
Univ Cambridge, *Madingley Hall*

28 February–2 March
1548 The Roman Empire in the second century £AFD
Urchfont Manor College, *Devizes*
ARCA

28 February–2 March
1549 Photography: using an SLR camera £92
1550 Wildlife of the Mediterranean (with Univ Essex, Continuing Education Dept) £81
1551 Spanish intermediate £82
Wansfell College, *Theydon Bois*
ARCA

BURTON MANOR COLLEGE

BURTON, SOUTH WIRRAL,
CHESHIRE. L64 5SJ.
Telephone 0151-336 5172

DAY, MIDWEEK AND WEEKEND COURSES

Painting, Drawing, Decorative Paint Finishes, Jewellery Making, Calligraphy, Developing Writing Power, Memoir Writing, Literature, Poetry, Psychology, Philosophy, Line Dancing, Belly Dancing, Music, Photography, Textiles, Embroidery, Floristry, Wine & Spirit Education Trust Certificate, History, Family and Local History, Heraldry, Bridge, Antiques, Egyptology, Gardening, Alexander Techniques, Aromatherapy, Crystal Healing, Feng Shui, Colour Healing, Meditation, Film Studies, Astronomy.

Also: **ISPA Diploma in Aromatherapy, Ceramic Restoration Diploma, China Painting Diploma & City & Guilds Enbroidery.**

Ring or write for details.

Burton Manor lies in the centre of Burton, one of the prettiest villages in Wirral. It is an impressive Manor House and it stands in thirty acres of private grounds with ornamental gardens, terraces and woodland with views across the Dee to the Welsh Hills. We offer exciting and interesting courses in comfortable, friendly surroundings. Our accommodation is in single or double rooms, some en-suite, with central heating, wash hand basins, tea and coffee making facilities. Wheelchair access and facilities for people with disabilities.

Easily accessible by road: 5 miles from M56. B.R. Chester and Liverpool.

28 February–2 March
1552 Understanding watercolour £AFD
Watercolour Weeks at Weobley, *Herefordshire*
ARCA

28 February–2 March
1553 Batik on silk £AFD
1554 Jewellery – rings with stone setting £AFD
1555 Lettercarving in stone and slate £AFD
1556 Watercolour beginners £AFD
1557 Bobbin lacemaking – East Midlands – Bucks Point, Bedfordshire and Torchon £AFD
1558 Experimental landscape painting £AFD
1559 Country garden style £AFD
West Dean College, *Chichester*
ARCA

March 1997

March 1997
1560 Oxford house party £AFD
Andante Travels, *Oxford*

March 1997
1561 Winter wildfowl £AFD
1562 Winter walking £AFD
1563 Winter landscapes £AFD
Field Studies Council at Preston Montford, *Shrewsbury*

1–2 March
1564 Kitemaking for the family £22
1565 Life weekend – all-comers £27
1566 Tile and china painting £21
The Gateway, *Shrewsbury*
Local accommodation is arranged separately on request.

1–31 March
1567 Basket making with cane £35*
1568 Sugarcraft £35*
1569 Eggcraft £35*
1570 Flower arranging £35*
1571 Bonsai £35*
1572 Fabric sculpture £35*
1573 Decorative interiors and paintwork £35*
1574 Stencilling £35*
1575 Needlecraft £35*
1576 Strawcraft £35*
1577 Machine knitting £35*
1578 Patchwork and quilting £35*
1579 Découpage – 3D £35*
1580 Découpage – traditional £35*
1581 Drawing, watercolours and oils £35*
1582 Gardening skills £35*
1583 Rush seating £35*
1584 Cane seating £35*
1585 Pottery – any Thursday £35*
1586 Music – any instrument 2 hours £35*
1587 Languages – one hour £15*
1588 Birdwatching £40*
1589 Furniture restoration – any 2 consecutive days £100
1590 Woodwork – any 3 consecutive days £150
Acorn Activities, *Herefordshire, Shropshire and Wales*
****Per day. Bookings can be made for any number of days.***

2–6 March
1591 Printmaking workshop £AFD
1592 Experimental stitched textiles £AFD
1593 Portrait photography £AFD
West Dean College, *Chichester*
ARCA

2–7 March
1594 Fabric collage and machine embroidery £200
Alston Hall Residential College, ***Preston***
ARCA

2–7 March
1595 Jewellery in silver £AFD
1596 Relief sculpture in wood £AFD
1597 Blacksmithing and wrought ironwork £AFD
West Dean College, ***Chichester***
ARCA

3–5 March
1598 Alexander Technique – follow-up £89
Alston Hall Residential College, ***Preston***
ARCA

3–5 March
1599 The secret world of Grieg's piano music £81
Wansfell College, ***Theydon Bois***
ARCA

3–6 March
1600 Foundation strings £135*
Benslow Music Trust, ***Hitchin***
ARCA
****Residential.***

3–7 March
1601 Creative embroidery from photographs £AFD
1602 Painting portraits in watercolour and oil £AFD
The Old Rectory, ***Fittleworth***
ARCA

5–7 March
1603 Alexander Technique £76
Lancashire College, ***Chorley***
ARCA

6–9 March
1604 Country weekend with music £105
Beaconhill, ***Deal, Kent***

7–9 March
1605 Cactus and Succulent Society annual course £80
Alston Hall Residential College, ***Preston***
ARCA

7–9 March
1606 Needlepoint lace £95
Belstead House, ***Ipswich***
ARCA

7–9 March
1607 The art of accompaniment £121*
Benslow Music Trust, ***Hitchin***
ARCA
****Residential.***

7–9 March
1608 Language weekend – French £59–£130
Brasshouse Centre, ***Birmingham***

7–9 March
1609 Space exploration £89
1610 Pathways to peace £89
Braziers, ***Ipsden***
ARCA

7–9 March
1611 Albigensian crusades £AFD
1612 French £AFD
1613 Writing for women by women £AFD
Dillington House, ***Ilminster***
ARCA

7–9 March
1614 A musical in a weekend £110
1615 Advanced camcorder and editing £110
Higham Hall, ***Cockermouth***
ARCA

7–9 March
1616 Creative lace £82
1617 China painting £82
Horncastle College, ***Horncastle***
ARCA

7–9 March

1618 It's on the tip of my tongue £87
1619 Circle dance and community £87
1620 Bridge for improvers £87

Knuston Hall, *Irchester*
ARCA

7–9 March

1621 Italian all levels £86
1622 Russian all levels £86
1623 Canvas work £86

Lancashire College, *Chorley*
ARCA

7–9 March

1624 British intelligence successes* £71–£99
1625 Liszt – a legendary composer-pianist* £71–£99

Maryland College, *Woburn*
ARCA
****Suitable for family groups.***

7–9 March

1626 From cylinders to CDs £AFD
1627 Flowers in watercolour £AFD
1628 C&G basketry – willow and hedgerow £AFD
1629 Teddy bears past and present £AFD
1630 Scandinavian embroidery £AFD
1631 Bridge – beginners follow on £AFD
1632 Writing crime fiction £AFD
1633 Talking with confidence £AFD
1634 The Brontë legend £AFD

Missenden Abbey, *Great Missenden*
ARCA

7–9 March

1635 Introduction to handwriting analysis £AFD
1636 Painting in any media £AFD
1637 Music in England 1919–1939 £AFD
1638 The A-Z of extending your home £AFD

The Old Rectory, *Fittleworth*
ARCA

7–9 March

1639 The building stones of England £AFD
1640 Medieval book production and use to c.1500 £AFD
1641 Falklands War £AFD
1642 *Götterdämmerung* £AFD

Univ Cambridge, *Madingley Hall*

7–9 March

1643 Plato's republic £AFD

Urchfont Manor College, *Devizes*
ARCA

7–9 March

1644 Linked French (advanced) £87
1645 Home sweet home £91

Wansfell College, *Theydon Bois*
ARCA

7–9 March

1646 Botanical illustration – spring bulbs £AFD
1647 Stained glass – traditional leading and copperfoiling £AFD
1648 Basic woodwork and carpentry skills £AFD
1649 Painters' masterclass £AFD
1650 Fabric collage in straight stitch and French knots £AFD
1651 Observational drawing £AFD

West Dean College, *Chichester*
ARCA

8–9 March

1652 Eastern art £AFD

Univ Manchester, *Manchester*

8–9 March

1653 Capital and community: London in the 16th and 17th centuries £29*

Univ Oxford, *Oxford*
****Tuition fee. Accommodation and meals available.***

8–9 March

1654 Tutorial – contemporary history £36
1655 Tutorial – music £36
1656 Tutorial – philosophy £36

Wedgwood Memorial College, *Barlaston*
ARCA

9–13 March
1657 Sculptural ceramics £AFD
1658 Drawing and painting on silk £AFD
West Dean College, *Chichester*
ARCA

9–14 March
1659 Carving birds £AFD
1660 Watercolour painting with pen, line and wash £AFD
West Dean College, *Chichester*
ARCA

9–15 March
1661 Country furniture and traditional chairmaking £AFD
West Dean College, *Chichester*
ARCA

10–14 March
1662 Wagner's ***Tristan*** £AFD
Higham Hall, *Cockermouth*
ARCA

13–16 March
1663 Walking weekend £105
Beaconhill, *Deal, Kent*

13–16 March
1664 Sign communication skills stage I module III £AFD
Lancashire College, *Chorley*
ARCA

14–16 March
1665 Music appreciation £80
1666 Chinese brush painting £80
Alston Hall Residential College, *Preston*
ARCA

14–16 March
1667 Double bass weekend £111*
1668 Intermediate recorder ensemble £111*
1669 Choose your piece for piano £111*
Benslow Music Trust, *Hitchin*
ARCA
****Residential.***

14–16 March
1670 Language weekend – Greek and Russian £59–£130
Brasshouse Centre, *Birmingham*

14–16 March
1671 Literature for all £89
1672 Survival French for holidays £89
Braziers, *Ipsden*
ARCA

14–16 March
1673 Novel into film – Jane Austen £95
Burton Manor College, *South Wirral*
ARCA

14–16 March
1674 Choral weekend £AFD
Dartington Hall, *Totnes, Devon*

14–16 March
1675 ***Der Rosenkavalier*** £AFD
1676 Daily life in the early church £AFD
Dillington House, *Ilminster*
ARCA

14–16 March
1677 Hawthorn bridge party £120/£125
Hawthorn Bridge, *Eastbourne, Sussex*

14–16 March
1678 Continental flower arranging £110
1679 Life drawing £125
1680 Fly fishing workshop £110
Higham Hall, *Cockermouth*
ARCA

14–16 March
1681 Purposeful photography £84
1682 Railways of Wales £84
The Hill Residential College, *Abergavenny*
ARCA

14–16 March

1683 Alexander Technique £82
1684 Pattern making techniques £82
1685 Spring flowers in watercolour £82

Horncastle College, *Horncastle*
ARCA

14–16 March

1686 A night at the opera £87
1687 Rubber stamp art £87
1688 Ships sea sand £87
1689 Folk weekend £87
1690 From cylinders to CDs £87

Knuston Hall, *Irchester*
ARCA

14–16 March

1691 Miniature painting £86
1692 French intermediate £86

Lancashire College, *Chorley*

14–16 March

1693 Logic puzzles and crosswords* £71–£99
1694 The Amish people and their quilts* £71–£99
1695 Garden history through paintings* £71–£99

Maryland College, *Woburn*
ARCA
Suitable for family groups.

14–16 March

1696 Alexander Technique for pianists £AFD
1697 Tai Ji £AFD
1698 Painting £AFD
1699 Passementerie £AFD
1700 C&G patchwork and quilting £AFD
1701 The last years of Tsarist Russia £AFD
1702 Art and design from 1910–1930 £AFD
1703 French literature £AFD

At the Misbourne School

1704 Chinese brush painting £AFD
1705 Oil painting for beginners £AFD
1706 Watercolour painting on silk £AFD
1707 Painting £AFD
1708 Sculpture with paste and paper £AFD
1709 Print and stitch £AFD
1710 Drama – exploring directing £AFD
1711 Traditional and modern upholstery £AFD
1712 The environment and sustainability – WWF workshop £AFD
1713 Jewellery £AFD
1714 Sugarcraft – Easter eggs £AFD

Missenden Abbey, *Great Missenden*
ARCA

14–16 March

1715 Introduction to Super Highway £AFD
1716 Map and compass for walkers £AFD
1717 Recorder weekend £AFD
1718 Freedom with watercolour £AFD

The Old Rectory, *Fittleworth*
ARCA

14–16 March

1719 Victorian Britain £AFD
1720 Flowers of Western Australia £AFD
1721 Italy in the early Christian period £AFD

Univ Cambridge, *Madingley Hall*

14–16 March

1722 Paganism to Christianity: the 14th centenary of the arrival of St Augustine in Kent £42*

Univ Oxford, *Oxford*
Tuition fee. Accommodation and meals available.

14–16 March

1723 Bedfordshire lace £AFD

Urchfont Manor College, *Devizes*
ARCA

14–16 March

1724 Bookbinding and repairs £96
1725 Linked German (intermediate) £88
1726 The road to power and glory part II £91

Wansfell College, *Theydon Bois*
ARCA

14–16 March
1727 Understanding watercolour £AFD
Watercolour Weeks at Weobley, ***Herefordshire***
ARCA

14–16 March
1728 Minor repairs and refinishing antique furniture £AFD
1729 Making jewellery and simple stone setting £AFD
1730 Glass engraving £AFD
1731 Life drawing £AFD
1732 Calligraphy – Italic for beginners £AFD
1733 Watercolour for beginners £AFD
West Dean College, ***Chichester***
ARCA

15–16 March
1734 Australian literature and culture £20
1735 Calligraphy – black letter and variations for today £22
1736 Pewtercraft £22
1737 Watercolour painting £20
The Gateway, ***Shrewsbury***
Local accommodation is arranged separately on request.

15–16 March
1738 Tutorial – women in literature £36
Wedgwood Memorial College, ***Barlaston***
ARCA

16–19 March
1739 Jewellery – making chains and beads £AFD
West Dean College, ***Chichester***
ARCA

16–21 March
1740 Winter painting from lens to landscaping £AFD
Higham Hall, ***Cockermouth***
ARCA

16–21 March
1741 Green-wood workshop – making a pole-lathe and a shaving-horse £AFD
1742 Mould-making and casting for sculpture £AFD
1743 Bookbinding and bookcraft £AFD
1744 Curtains – lined and interlined with hand-made headings £AFD
1745 Landscape painting – all media £AFD
West Dean College, ***Chichester***
ARCA

17–21 March
1746 A touch of gold (calligraphy) £AFD
1747 Landscape and gardens in mixed media £AFD
1748 Viola da Gamba in consort £AFD
The Old Rectory, ***Fittleworth***
ARCA

19–21 March
1749 Pruning – principles and practice £AFD
West Dean College, ***Chichester***
ARCA

19–24 March
1750 Cabinet making – part 2 £AFD
West Dean College, ***Chichester***
ARCA

20–23 March
1751 The countryside in spring £105
Beaconhill, ***Deal, Kent***

21–23 March
1752 Annual astronomy course £80
Alston Hall Residential College, ***Preston***
ARCA

21–23 March
1753 Elementary wind chamber music £111*
Benslow Music Trust, ***Hitchin***
ARCA
***Residential.*

21–23 March
1754 Goldwork embroidery £95
1755 Flamenco dancing £97
1756 Marcher castles £95
Burton Manor College, *South Wirral*
ARCA

21–23 March
1757 Calligraphy £AFD
1758 Watercolour £AFD
Dartington Hall, *Totnes, Devon*

21–23 March
1759 Silk painting £AFD
1760 Writing for children £AFD
1761 Eternal Egypt £AFD
1762 Darkroom photography £AFD
Dillington House, *Ilminster*
ARCA

21–23 March
1763 Baroque chamber music £108/£116
Hawkwood College, *Stroud*
ARCA

21–23 March
1764 Tassel making £110
1765 Creative writing – the art of lying £110
1766 The Englishman's home is his castle £110
Higham Hall, *Cockermouth*
ARCA

21–23 March
1767 Silversmithing £82
Horncastle College, *Horncastle*
ARCA

21–23 March
1768 Dowsing and divining £87
1769 Rambling £87
1770 Calligraphy £87
Knuston Hall, *Irchester*
ARCA

21–23 March
1771 Portrait painting* £71–£99
1772 Advanced German* £71–£99
Maryland College, *Woburn*
ARCA
Suitable for family groups.

21–23 March
1773 French conversation (intermediate) £55
Meirionnydd Languages, *North Wales*

21–23 March
1774 Silverwork and jewellery £AFD
1775 Wet in wet £AFD
1776 Beekeeping for all £AFD
1777 Spirits of earth and air £AFD
The Old Rectory, *Fittleworth*
ARCA

21–23 March
1778 Music appreciation £AFD
Pendrell Hall College, *Codsall Wood*
ARCA

21–23 March
1779 Georgian Cambridge £AFD
1780 German weekend £AFD
1781 Early Victorian Cambridge: the University and its reform £AFD
1782 Reading classical Greek £AFD
Univ Cambridge, *Madingley Hall*

21–23 March
1783 Geological miscellany XII £AFD
1784 Massage for relaxation £AFD
Urchfont Manor College, *Devizes*
ARCA

21–23 March
1785 English landscape artists £91
1786 Milestones to the new millennium £81
Wansfell College, *Theydon Bois*
ARCA

21–23 March
1787 Social history – fish and chips £65
Wedgwood Memorial College, *Barlaston*
ARCA

21–23 March
1788 Relief printing – linocuts and wood engraving £AFD
West Dean College, *Chichester*
ARCA

21–24 March
1789 Framing workshop £AFD
1790 Enamelling on copper and steel £AFD
1791 Flowers and still life – beginner's watercolour £AFD
1792 Further techniques in miniature painting £AFD
West Dean College, *Chichester*
ARCA

21–26 March
1793 Starting to write and making progress £AFD
West Dean College, *Chichester*
ARCA

22–23 March
1794 Painting £25
1795 Willow basket making – ovals £22
The Gateway, *Shrewsbury*
Local accommodation is arranged separately on request.

22–23 March
1796 Watercolours for beginners stages I and II £AFD
Pendrell Hall College, *Codsall Wood*
ARCA

23–28 March
1797 Small silverwork £AFD
Higham Hall, *Cockermouth*
ARCA

23–28 March
1798 Calligraphy £218
Knuston Hall, *Irchester*
ARCA

23–28 March
1799 Landscape painting £165–£210
Snowdonia National Park Centre, *Maentwrog*
ARCA

24–25 March
1800 E M Forster £22
1801 French Impressionists £22
The Gateway, *Shrewsbury*
Local accommodation is arranged separately on request.

24–27 March
1802 Chamber music for strings, wind and piano £131
Alston Hall Residential College, *Preston*
ARCA

24–27 March
1803 Flower painting – various media £143
Burton Manor College, *South Wirral*
ARCA

24–27 March
1804 Stained glass £49
The Gateway, *Shrewsbury*
Local accommodation is arranged separately on request.

24–27 March
1805 Early music – recorder £105
Wedgwood Memorial College, *Barlaston*
ARCA

24–28 March
1806 Mozart's last year (1791) £AFD
1807 Learn to paint with watercolours £AFD
1808 Drawing for the terrified I £AFD
1809 Painting miniatures £AFD
1810 Hat trimming £AFD
1811 Bead needle weaving for jewellery £AFD
1812 Wildfowl woodcarving £AFD
1813 Life stories £AFD
Missenden Abbey, *Great Missenden*
ARCA

26 March–4 April
1814 Making musical instruments £AFD
West Dean College, *Chichester*
ARCA

27–31 March
1815 Easter course – the music, art, architecture and social history of France £160
Alston Hall Residential College, *Preston*
ARCA

27–31 March
1816 A country Easter £155
Beaconhill, *Deal, Kent*

27–31 March
1817 Folklore of Easter
1818 Country walks
1819 Writing and reading poetry £180
Braziers, *Ipsden*
ARCA

27–31 March
1820 Easter painting workshop £180
1821 Easter bridge £181
Burton Manor College, *South Wirral*
ARCA

27–31 March
1822 Easter houseparty £AFD
The Old Rectory, *Fittleworth*
ARCA

27–31 March
1823 Bridge £162
Wansfell College, *Theydon Bois*
ARCA

27–31 March
1824 Getting the best from your camera £AFD
West Dean College, *Chichester*
ARCA

28–30 March
1825 Understanding watercolour £AFD
Watercolour Weeks at Weobley, *Herefordshire*
ARCA

28–30 March
1826 Imaginative ways with watercolour £AFD
1827 Surrealism in painting £AFD
West Dean College, *Chichester*
ARCA

28–31 March
1828 Friends of Higham weekend £AFD
Higham Hall, *Cockermouth*
ARCA

28–31 March
1829 The four seasons in art and music £AFD
1830 Learn to paint with watercolours £AFD
1831 Spring landscape painting £AFD
1832 Needlelace, topiary and stitch £AFD
1833 Counted thread embroidery £AFD
1834 Writing poetry £AFD
Missenden Abbey, *Great Missenden*
ARCA

28 March–4 April
1835 Alberni masterclass £AFD
1836 Practical painting £AFD
Univ Cambridge, *Madingley Hall*

29–31 March
1837 Poetry of Yeutushenko £55
Meirionnydd Languages, *North Wales*

30 March–4 April
1838 Pottery general £AFD
1839 Watercolour and lettering £AFD
1840 Shapes in the landscape – mixed media £AFD
West Dean College, *Chichester*
ARCA

31 March–4 April
1841 Batik workshop £178
1842 Learn to paint and draw £166
Alston Hall Residential College, *Preston*
ARCA

31 March–4 April
1843 Taking liberties with fabrics £AFD
1844 Painting £AFD
1845 The creative self £AFD
1846 So you think you can't draw £AFD
1847 Goldwork embroidery £AFD
1848 India in literature £AFD
Missenden Abbey, *Great Missenden*
ARCA

Study Tours and Learning Holidays Abroad

■ ■ ■ ■

October 1996

□ □ □ □

30 September–25 October
1849 Italian (all levels) £AFD
1850 High Renaissance and beyond £AFD
1851 Drawing £AFD
1852 Italian cooking £AFD
British Institute of Florence, *Italy*

Each Monday
1853 Learn Spanish in Spain £AFD
Top Mark UK, *Spain*
1854 Learn French in Normandy £AFD
Top Mark UK, *France*

1–5 October
1855 Painting/sketching £359
1856 Art and history discovery walks/tours in Nice £359
LSG Theme Holidays, *Nice (Côte d'Azur)*

1–20 October
1857 The natural history of South Australia £2420
FSC Overseas, *South Australia*

8–15 October
1858 Discovery tour of the treasures of Burgundy £669
LSG Theme Holidays, *Beaune, Auxerre*

12–22 October
1859 Autumn in Andalucia: Southern Spain and Doñana National Park £1095
FSC Overseas, *Andalucia, Spain*

19–26 October
1860 Art and architecture in Florence £680
Univ Nottingham, *Florence, Italy*

25–28 October
1861 Art in Siena £AFD
British Institute of Florence, *Italy*

26 October–5 November
1862 Autumn in Andalucia: Southern Spain and Doñana National Park £1095
FSC Overseas, *Andalucia, Spain*

27 October–3 November
1863 Carthage and classical Northern Tunisia with David Allen £780*
Andante Travels, *Tunis, Ain Draham and Hammamet*
£65 single supplement.

28 October–8 November
1864 Italian (all levels) £AFD
1865 Dawn of the Renaissance £AFD
British Institute of Florence, *Italy*

30 October–3 November
1866 Byzantium and Ottoman Istanbul with Barnaby Rogerson £700*
Andante Travels, *Istanbul*
£70 single supplement.

■ ■ ■ ■

November 1996

□ □ □ □

Each Monday
1867 Learn Spanish in Spain £AFD
Top Mark UK, *Spain*
1868 Learn French in Normandy £AFD
Top Mark UK, *France*

1–29 November
1869 A natural history tour of New Zealand £3800
FSC Overseas, *New Zealand*

3–10 November
1870 Venice and her islands with Graham Tite £900*
Andante Travels, *Venice*
£80 single supplement.

5–25 November
1871 Journeying through Chile to Tierra del Fuego £3750
FSC Overseas, *Chile, Argentina*

11–22 November
1872 Italian (all levels) £AFD
1873 Michelangelo and his influence £AFD
1874 Italian opera £AFD
British Institute of Florence, *Italy*

12–28 November
1875 Tropical forests in Thailand: their diversity, peoples and conservation £1750
FSC Overseas, *Thailand*

25 November–17 December
1876 Italian (all levels) £AFD
1877 Florentine Renaissance £AFD
1878 Drawing £AFD
1879 Italian cooking £AFD
British Institute of Florence, *Italy*

■ ■ ■ ■

December 1996

□ □ □ □

Each Monday
1880 Learn Spanish in Spain £AFD
Top Mark UK, *Spain*
1881 Learn French in Normandy £AFD
Top Mark UK, *France*

5–8 December
1882 Christmas markets weekend in Germany £AFD
Brasshouse Centre, *Eifel Mountains area*

6–9 December
1883 Festive Paris £269
LSG Theme Holidays, *Paris*

21–28 December
1884 Christmas in north Cyprus with Naomi Hamilton and Müge evketoglu £900*
Andante Travels, *Girne (Kyrenia) and Salamis, N. Cyprus*
£80 single supplement.

■ ■ ■ ■

January 1997

□ □ □ □

Each Monday
1885 Learn Spanish in Spain £AFD
Top Mark UK, *Spain*
1886 Learn French in Normandy £AFD
Top Mark UK, *France*

2–12 January
1887 Botany and geology on Tenerife and Lanzarote £1100
FSC Overseas, *Canary Islands*

6–18 January
1888 Architecture in Florence £AFD
British Institute of Florence, *Italy*

6–31 January
1889 Italian (all levels) £AFD
1890 Drawing £AFD
1891 Italian cooking £AFD
British Institute of Florence, *Italy*

20 January–1 February
1892 Dawn of the Renaissance £AFD
British Institute of Florence, *Italy*

■ ■ ■ ■

February 1997

□ □ □ □

February 1997
1893 Private Florence £AFD
Andante Travels, *Florence*

Each Monday
1894 Learn Spanish in Spain £AFD
Top Mark UK, *Spain*
1895 Learn French in Normandy £AFD
Top Mark UK, *France*

3–28 February
1896 Italian (all levels) £AFD
1897 Florentine Renaissance £AFD
1898 Drawing £AFD
1899 Italian cooking £AFD
British Institute of Florence, *Italy*

8–15 February
1900 Art in Florence £AFD
British Institute of Florence, *Italy*

20–24 February
1901 Nice Carnival ***Flowers and Fireworks*** £419
LSG Theme Holidays, *Nice (Côte d'Azur)*

28 February–2 March
1902 Michelangelo £AFD
British Institute of Florence, *Italy*

■ ■ ■ ■

March 1997

□ □ □ □

March 1997
1903 Andante in Venice £AFD
Andante Travels, *Venice*
1904 Ancient Tunisia at Easter £AFD
Andante Travels, *Tunis, Hammamet, Kairouan and others*
1905 Roman Spain (Tarraconensis) £AFD
Andante Travels, *Tarragona, Girona, Barcelona*

Each Monday
1906 Learn Spanish in Spain £AFD
Top Mark UK, *Spain*
1907 Learn French in Normandy £AF
Top Mark UK, *France*

3–28 March
1908 Italian (all levels) £AFD
1909 High Renaissance and beyond £AFD
1910 Drawing £AFD
1911 Italian cooking £AFD
British Institute of Florence, *Italy*

17–27 March
1912 Spring in Andalucia: Southern Spain and Doñana National Park £1095
FSC Overseas, *Andalucia, Spain*

26 March–2 April
1913 Walking on Guernsey: Easter explorations £700
FSC Overseas, *Guernsey*

26 March–9 April
1914 Easter on Seychelles: an introduction to tropical ecology £AFD
FSC Overseas, *Seychelles*

27 March–10 April
1915 Tambopata: a wildlife El Dorado in Peru £AFD
FSC Overseas, *Peru*

31 March–11 April
1916 Italian (all levels) £AFD
1917 The Florentine sculptors £AFD
British Institute of Florence, *Italy*

ENQUIRY COUPON

To find out more about a learning holiday you have seen listed in this book, complete this coupon and send it DIRECT to the Organiser. Please do not send it to NIACE.

Please send me further information on the following learning holiday(s) as advertised by you in *Time to Learn*.

____

____

____

____

Please fill in your name and address on the reverse side ▶

ENQUIRY COUPON

To find out more about a learning holiday you have seen listed in this book, complete this coupon and send it DIRECT to the Organiser. Please do not send it to NIACE.

Please send me further information on the following learning holiday(s) as advertised by you in *Time to Learn*.

____

____

____

____

Please fill in your name and address on the reverse side ▶

ENQUIRY COUPON

To find out more about a learning holiday you have seen listed in this book, complete this coupon and send it DIRECT to the Organiser. Please do not send it to NIACE.

Please send me further information on the following learning holiday(s) as advertised by you in *Time to Learn*.

____

____

____

____

Please fill in your name and address on the reverse side ▶

Name: ____________________

____

Address: ____________________

____

____

____

____________________ **Postcode:** ____________

Name: ____________________

____

Address: ____________________

____

____

____

____________________ **Postcode:** ____________

Name: ____________________

____

Address: ____________________

____

____

____

____________________ **Postcode:** ____________

ORDER FORM

April – September 1997

Published January 1997

Price: £4.25 post free in UK

(Overseas airmail £7.00; Overseas surface mail £5.50)

Please send me copy/copies of *Time to Learn*
April – September 1997

I enclose payment of £_________.

(Please make cheques and postal orders payable to: NIACE. Overseas orders should pay by sterling cheque drawn on a UK bank or by sterling money order. We are unable to accept orders without payment.)

Send with payment to:
Publications Sales, NIACE,
21 De Montfort Street, Leicester LE1 7GE

Alternatively, take this completed form to your bookseller to order on your behalf.

Name: ____________________________________

Address: ____________________________________

____

____

____

Trade orders to: Central Books Ltd, 99 Wallis Road, London E9 5LN
(Tel. 0181 986 4854; Fax. 0181 533 5821)

Subject Index

The numbers listed in this index refer to the individual numbers assigned to each learning holiday; *they are not page numbers.* To guide you, the learning holidays numbered from 1 to 390 are being held during October 1996; 391 to 796 during November 1996; 797 to 958 in December 1996; 959 to 1247 during January 1997; 1248 to 1559 in February 1997 and 1560 to 1848 during March 1997. Numbers 1849 to 1917 cover learning holidays and study tours abroad.